HOW YOU CAN HELP

A Guide For Families of Psychiatric Hospital Patients

Herbert S. Korpell, M.D.

The American Psychiatric Press, Inc., an independent corporation affiliated with the American Psychiatric Association, publishes psychiatric literature for professionals. This book is one of many titles planned for publication which expands the scope of the Press into publications of interest to the general public. The first three to be released include:

How You Can Help: A Guide for Families of Psychiatric Hospital Patients
    By Herbert S. Korpell, M.D. (casebound) #48-016-5 $15.95; (paperback)
    #48-026-2 $9.95

Depression and its Treatment: Help for the Nation's #1 Mental Problem
    By John H. Greist, M.D. and James W. Jefferson, M.D. (paperback)
    #48-025-4 $7.95

The American Psychiatric Association's Psychiatric Glossary (paperback)
    #48-027-0 $7.95

1400 K Street, N.W.
Washington, D.C. 20005

HOW YOU CAN HELP

A Guide For Families of Psychiatric Hospital Patients

Herbert S. Korpell, M.D.

American
Psychiatric
Press, Inc.

Note: The author has worked to ensure that all information in this book concerning drug dosages, schedules, and routes of administration is accurate as of the time of publication and consistent with standards set by the United States Food and Drug Administration and the general medical community. As medical research and practice advance, however, therapeutic standards may change. For this reason and because human and mechanical errors sometimes occur, it is recommended that readers follow the advice of a physician who is directly involved in their care or the care of a member of their family.

Library of Congress Cataloging in Publication data
Main entry under title:

Korpell, Herbert S.
  How you can help.

  Bibliography: p.
  1. Psychiatric hospital care. I. Title. [DNLM: 1. Mental disorders—Popular works. 2. Family—Popular works. 3. Hospitalization—Popular works. 4. Hospitals, Psychiatric—Popular works. WM 100 K845h]
RC439.K644 1984   362.2'1   83-25750
ISBN 0-88048-026-2

Printed in the U.S.A.

DEDICATION

To my wife Kathy

ABOUT THE AUTHOR

Herbert S. Korpell, M.D., decided to become a psychiatrist when he was thirteen years old. He majored in psychology in college and earned his way with scholarships and by leading his own dance band.

During medical school he studied with Eric Berne, M.D.; Fritz Perls, M. D.; Ronald Laing, M.D.; and at Anna Freud's Hampstead Clinic in London.

Dr. Korpell has a private practice in Berkeley, California. He is board-certified and specializes in hospital psychiatry. He is married and has one daughter.

CONTENTS

ACKNOWLEDGEMENTS

I would like to thank the many people who encouraged me and helped me write this book, especially Tita Braley, Heidi Covarelli, Lois Danton, Louis Dickens, Ph.D.; Paul DiGaudio, M.D.; Susan Dubin, Paul Gillette, Ph.D.; Kathleen Korpell, Millicent Hintermeister, Robert Mann, Donald McCormack, Melvin Lipsett, M.D.; Donna Porter, R.N.; Anthony Rienzi, M.D.; Pat Silverstein, R.N.; Russell Silverstein, M.D.; and Marilyn Tull, R.N.

1

What This Book Is About
And How It Can Help You

Your husband comes home drunk again on payday; he has no money, and you have no idea how to pay the bills.

Your wife has mentioned casually that she sometimes thinks life isn't worth living, and now you discover that she secretly has been saving up her sleeping pills.

Your teenage son has seemed for a long time to be in a world of his own. He often says things that make no sense to you, and he claims to hear voices when you know that no one else is in his room. When you try to talk about what's troubling him, he gets angry and threatens to become violent.

If you are in a situation like this, you probably feel helpless and confused, and maybe even near panic. You know that something is terribly wrong, but you don't know what to do about it.

If the problem has existed for any length of time, you probably have sought help from a psychiatrist, a psychologist, some other therapist, or a social service agency. Even though you may have been favorably impressed with the person or agency that you consulted, you may feel that your husband or wife or son is not making enough progress and that you yourself should be doing more to assist in his or her recovery.

Sometimes, a psychiatrist will determine that a patient should be hospitalized. Such cases are far from rare. In fact, one-third of the hospital beds in the United States today are occupied by psychiatric patients. (That's right, one of every three hospital patients in America today is being treated for psychiatric problems.)

If the need for hospitalization is recognized early, the patient's problems can be dealt with quickly and effectively. Often hospitalization will be very brief—a few days or, at most, a few weeks, followed by continuing treatment in an office or clinic while the patient lives at home. Yet, if hospitalization is recommended for your relative, you may be frightened and unsure of what to do.

The aim of this book is to explain what can be done and how you can ensure that your relative will have the best care possible.

This book is about ways of seeking help, of evaluating facilities that are available to you, and of dealing with loved ones who may not agree that they need help. It includes a description of what happens in psychiatric hospitals—what kind of treatment is offered, how patients typically spend their time, how families and friends are informed about a patient's condition. It also will offer advice on how to deal with the various members of the treatment team and how to give your hospitalized relative the assistance and support that can contribute greatly to a speedy and complete recovery.

Much of this information will, I hope, be of interest to the general public and will help encourage enlightened decision-making on issues such as patients' rights, hospital funding, and involuntary hospitalization. The book will also, I believe, prove useful to mental health professionals and to people in such fields as medicine, law, education, and public service. Patients themselves may wish to read it and will, I fervently hope, find it helpful.

However, I am writing primarily for the families of patients— the spouses, parents, siblings, children, or other relatives who want desperately to do the "right" thing but do not know quite what to do.

The book is not—it most emphatically is *not*—intended as a substitute for professional care. Do-it-yourself psychiatry is no less dangerous than do-it-yourself internal medicine. Decisions you make about your relative's treatment must be based on the facts of the individual case as they will be explained to you by the psychiatrist and other professionals whom you consult. My aim is to provide background information which will help you in understanding and evaluating those facts and in making prudent judgments about them.

UNDERSTANDING PSYCHIATRIC PROBLEMS

The word psychiatrist derives from two Greek words, "psyche," mind, and "iatros," physician.

The idea that a person can have a disorder of the mind which requires healing might at first seem both strange and mysterious. However, the sensations and behavior involved in such disorders are probably very close to some experiences that you yourself have had.

For example, if someone close to you died, you probably underwent a period of grief. You may have become withdrawn and unable to concentrate on your work. You may have gone through times when you cried easily and felt a need to retire from the world.

These reactions are normal. In fact, something would be wrong if you did not react in some way to the loss of your loved one.

Now, for a moment, imagine a person who behaves in the same way with no apparent cause. This behavior describes a form of depression, the most prevalent psychiatric disorder, which afflicts tens of millions of Americans.

Let's look at some other examples of mental disturbance:

If someone cheats you in a business transaction, you may get angry. If the stakes are high enough, you may want revenge. You might even feel, under extreme circumstances, that you'd like to kill your antagonist.

Of course, even if you believed that you would be justified in blowing the person's head off, in the end you would not go out and get a shotgun and actually commit murder. But there are people who will do just that, sometimes with little or no apparent provocation. The difference is that you had the impulse to do something destructive but controlled yourself, while someone else had a similar impulse and acted on it.

Most mental disorders, of course, do not lead to criminal acts; yet evidence of an emotional problem may be obvious to anyone who knows the person's situation. For example, you may know people who use consciousness-altering drugs to avoid feelings, such as depression or anxiety, which the drugs (at least initially) alleviate. Or you may know people who gamble away the family grocery money because they may feel an overwhelming compulsion to do so.

Sometimes mental problems become so severe that people cannot take care of themselves. If you have ever gotten drunk, you can appreciate this sort of helplessness. In a state of deep inebriation you cannot walk or talk normally, you are unable to think clearly, and your feelings are different from usual. Heavy drinking can lead to "blackouts," periods during which the drinker is awake but cannot remember later. After a prolonged period of heavy drinking, with-drawal of alcohol can cause a person to enter a confused state called delirium tremens ("the DTs") and see things which do not exist (for example, little pink elephants or snakes).

Imagine someone who has such experiences without being inebriated and you will have a good idea of the mental state of some psychiatric patients. You probably will agree that the best interests of the person—and of society—may be served if the person spends some time in a hospital for their own good.

Let me emphasize that I am not talking now about people whose ideas or behavior are simply unconventional. For instance, a man may believe that the earth is being visited by representatives of a far-away civilization. This is not of itself evidence of psychiatric disturbance; indeed, some respected scientists do not rule out the possibility that extraterrestrial civilizations have sent emissaries to our planet. But if the man becomes convinced that a spaceship is about to pick him up, and if he begins preparing for his immediate departure from earth, he may be unable to attend to his terrestrial responsibilities. He may hear voices which tell him to do dangerous things—for example, to board the spaceship by jumping from the roof of a ten-story building. Or he may believe that the only way his children will be able to join him on the flight is if they are purged of earthly evil by being strangled or poisoned.

Let's look at another example:

The psychiatric diagnostic term "paranoid" is used in everyday language to describe people who are overly suspicious. Someone may believe, for instance, that others are conspiring against and perhaps even planning to murder him or her.

Such beliefs are not always unreasonable. The history of the past few decades provides many examples of spouses, politicians, business executives, and others in all walks of life who were murdered or otherwise victimized by conspirators.

But some people who believe themselves to be victims, or potential victims, of a conspiracy are deluded. They may become frightened that someone is out to get them—a spouse, a business acquaintance, a governmental agency, a secret society. If they reveal their suspicions to others, they may be ridiculed. They may then decide that they must act on their own to ward off the threat. Some homicides have grown out of such delusions.

But who has not at one time or another suspected that someone wished us ill? What is the line that separates warranted suspicions from unwarranted suspicions, logical ones from illogical ones, reasonable ones from unreasonable ones?

In sum, the things that bother the typical psychiatric patient are not all that far removed from the things that bother you and me. Even the most complicated psychiatric conditions are not so strange that the average person cannot relate to them. Everyone has problems, and serious problems are much more widespread than many people want to acknowledge.

SHOULD PEOPLE BE HOSPITALIZED AGAINST THEIR WILL?

This is a serious issue, but it should not be permitted to obscure the no-less-serious matter of society's responsibilities to its members.

For instance, a person may become so depressed that he or she wants to commit suicide. One might argue that suicide is not antisocial—it will not hurt anyone else—and that we have the right to do as we wish with our own lives.

The merits or demerits of the argument notwithstanding, suicide is an irrevocable act. The general feeling in society is that people who are suicidal should be given a chance to reconsider and should be placed in a protected environment for at least a few days to think things over. In many cases, they will change their minds and go on to live satisfying and fulfilling lives.

The usual problem is not that people are "locked up" against their wishes but that the desirability of their being hospitalized is not recognized soon enough—not recognized until they have inflicted beatings on a spouse or child, not recognized until they have done permanent damage to themselves with drugs, not recognized until they have gone "berserk" and murdered someone.

UNDERSTANDING PSYCHIATRIC HOSPITALS

Psychiatric hospitals fall into two categories, described in medical language according to the expected duration of the patient's stay, acute care and long-term care.

An acute care hospital is one where patients usually go first, and it is designed for short-term treatment. But don't let the word "acute" alarm you. As used in psychiatry, it does not mean sharp or severe as in everyday English, but rather "of short duration," in contrast to "chronic" or "long-term." In other words, an acute care facility is one where patients' problems receive prompt and intensive attention.

In a high percentage of cases, the patient will be discharged within a short period of time. Some patients will require no follow-up treatment. Others will receive follow-up as outpatients. In cases where discharge is not deemed advisable, the patient will usually be transferred to another facility for long-term care.

The thought of psychiatric hospitalization is far more scary to most people than it should be. Few people would be alarmed about being admitted to a general hospital for tests or for an appendectomy. The typical acute care psychiatric hospital is not that much different from the typical general hospital. Doctors and nurses work with patients; the main difference is that they deal mainly with psychiatric problems rather than physical problems. And the typical long-term psychiatric facility is much like a convalescent home—the principal difference is that patients' problems are mainly psychiatric rather than physical.

This book will deal chiefly with acute care hospitals, because they are the only institutions with which the vast majority of patients will have contact. Of course, not all hospitals function in exactly the same way, so it is possible that the hospital with which you are involved will differ in some respects from the models discussed here. However, the basic situation at most psychiatric hospitals will be very much like what you read about here.

Many acute care psychiatric facilities are simply wards in a local general hospital. Others are independent institutions, but basically they function in the same way. The process of getting admitted is much like that of entering a general hospital, with the same procedures of qualifying for insurance, paying a deposit, signing forms, and so on.

The admission procedure includes an assessment of the patient's medical state and may involve a physical examination and laboratory tests. This is because a patient's physical condition is important if psychiatric drugs are to be used and also because physical and mental disturbances often are connected.

Indeed, many mental problems have been linked to biologic disorders. Depression sometimes can be traced to genetic influences, hormonal imbalances, or other biochemical factors. The so-called organic mental disorders, including senility and drug-induced mental states, have obvious biological bases. Mental retardation often can be explained biochemically. And such disorders as dyslexia (impaired ability to read), enuresis (bed-wetting), and anorexia and bulimia (abnormal appetite for food) suggest biological influence.

A medical problem occasionally will masquerade as a mental problem, as in some cases of hormonal imbalance. For example, a person who is depressed may seem to be reacting to circumstances when actually the culprit is a thyroid deficiency or a problem involving secretions of the adrenal glands.

The psychiatrist's first task is to investigate the factors which may be responsible for the signs and symptoms of the patient's mental disorder. ("Signs," in medical talk, are things which can be discovered in an examination but of which the patient may not be aware—for example, low blood sugar or an absence of the knee-jerk reflex. "Symptoms" are experiences of which the patient complains but which the examiner may be unable to detect—for example, headache or nausea.)

While looking for physical causes of mental disturbance, psychiatrists are careful not to cling to physical explanations in order to avoid a psychiatric diagnosis. Sometimes there is a tendency to do this because of the stigma which society attaches to mental disorder; most people would much rather be told they have a physical problem than a mental one. However, while it may be tempting to conclude that a patient hears voices because of a vitamin deficiency, the problem probably is considerably more complex. Likewise, someone might hypothesize that depression following menopause is due to a simple hormonal deficiency; but if hormone pills don't solve the problem, other hypotheses must be developed.

At every step along the way, the psychiatrist makes judgments about what the patient's problem may be and about what diagnostic and therapeutic approaches must be pursued. For example, although it is true that the symptoms of a brain tumor are in some instances identical to the symptoms of a nonorganic psychiatric disorder (that is, one without a known physical cause), the psychiatrist would not order extensive testing for brain tumor in every case. Instead, the whole clinical picture will be looked at for diagnostic hypotheses. Every diagnostic procedure carries some risk which must be weighed against the probable benefits, and, when a probable diagnosis is obvious, the psychiatrist won't go looking for a rare disease.

In the course of making a diagnosis, the psychiatrist works closely with colleagues in other disciplines. Often he or she asks a psychologist to perform psychometric testing. In this procedure, a patient answers questions, makes drawings, and comments on inkblots and pictures. Also, a social worker might talk with the patient and the patient's family about living conditions, employment, eligibility for welfare, and what to do after discharge. A dietician might recommend foods that should be eaten and others that should be avoided.

If the patient is a teenager, arrangements may have to be made to continue his or her schooling. Some patients might have medical conditions which require the attention of an internist or other specialist. Some patients might need help with problems of hearing, vision, or bodily coordination.

After the initial evaluations, plans are developed for treatment. Usually the problem will be one the psychiatrist has dealt with in the past, and the approach will be one that has worked before. He or she will have some idea of what has to be done and how things will go. He or she also should be able to estimate what difficulties might arise and how long the patient will have to remain in the hospital.

But every case has its special characteristics. A disobedient teenager with destructive behavior cannot be handled in the same way as a frightened victim of senility who needs help to eat or take a bath. A program for alcoholics or drug abusers will not be the same as one for other people who may display similar symptoms. Thus, the plan of treatment is tailored to each patient's problems and circumstances.

When the psychiatrist draws up a treatment plan, he or she lists specific problems and defines goals. He or she also makes an assessment of how to pursue these goals, how to measure progress, and how long treatment should take. Of course, the plan may change as time passes and the results of early therapy are assessed.

Much of the psychiatrist's time in the hospital is spent talking to patients and their relatives about problems and coordinating the efforts of the staff. Some psychiatric conditions can be helped greatly with medications, and it is the psychiatrist's job to determine which medications are best suited and to prescribe them. He or she also supervises other forms of treatment that may be ordered; for example, some patients who have difficulty expressing themselves directly may be able to express themselves indirectly by drawing pictures or through other non-verbal activities.

UNDERSTANDING YOUR ROLE

This book will tell you a great many things about psychiatric hospitalization, but—I cannot make the point too strongly—it should not be regarded as a primer for do-it-yourself diagnosis or therapy.

I think you can learn a great deal from the case reports that I present, but they should not be regarded as a direct parallel to the situation of your mentally-disturbed relative. The cases presented throughout the book are composites illustrating typical situations. They portray events which occur over and over among people with psychiatric problems. Identifiable resemblances to real persons, living or dead, are purely coincidental.

While using this book to understand better the problems of your relative, it should not be regarded as a substitute for discussion with your relative's psychiatrist or other members of the treatment team. Ask these people about anything that you do not understand.

Patients who require hospitalization obviously need assistance. The psychiatrist and other members of the staff can best advise you about what part you might play in your relative's recovery.

Likewise, while I encourage you to be helpful, please remember that you are not expected to—and cannot—run your relative's life. The patient should learn to do this independently as soon as possible. The purpose of this book is to help you help the patient accomplish this objective as soon as possible. In the chapters ahead, I'll offer many specific suggestions about how you can help.

2

Who Needs
Psychiatric Hospitalization?

Most people have emotional problems at some time in their lives. When problems become severe, they can interfere with a person's ability to function. Usually people try to deal with the problems on their own at first, then seek professional help when efforts at self-help prove unsuccessful.

Treatment for emotional problems usually is successful on an outpatient basis, which is generally preferable because it avoids interrupting the patient's life and is much less costly. However, sometimes treatment in a hospital might be more effective. This is particularly true when patients become dangerous to themselves or to others or when they behave in ways that people around them do not tolerate.

DECIDING THAT HOSPITALIZATION
IS DESIRABLE

A decision about hospitalization is always difficult, and it is not a decision that you can make for your relative. But you might be surprised to learn that sometimes patients *want* to go into a hospital. Although most patients resist treatment to some degree, those who recognize a need for it and arrange it by themselves are usually more motivated and get better more quickly.

Unfortunately, a patient may want to enter a hospital but be unable to gain admission. A case in point:

> *A 37-year-old woman had spent years being treated for schizophrenia as an outpatient and in hospitals, halfway houses, and day treatment centers. A year after her most recent discharge, she suffered a series of mishaps. Her apartment was burglarized, she lost a part-time job, and she was molested on the street.*
>
> *In response, she began undergoing a process that is known as "decompensation." That is, she did not have the inner resources to combat what was happening to her, and her grip on reality grew weaker. She became progressively more fearful of her environment and decided to return to the city where she had grown up. Once there, she felt no better and tried to admit herself to a private psychiatric hospital.*
>
> *She was told that no bed was available, and was referred to the psychiatric emergency room of the county hospital. The psychiatrist who evaluated her felt that she could benefit from hospitalization, but, since she was not extremely disturbed or violent, and there were only two empty psychiatric beds still available to serve the entire county, she was denied admission.*
>
> *She knew that she would only continue to decompensate if she did not get help. But in her increasingly disorganized state of mind, she was unable to arrange for treatment as an outpatient. She continued to decompensate—to grow more confused and frightened and visibly disturbed—until finally, wandering along the highway and being narrowly missed by passing automobiles, she was picked up by the police. Now the county hospital deemed her sufficiently disturbed and admitted her.*

Ideally, the patient, the patient's family, and the patient's psychotherapist will agree that hospitalization is desirable. Often, however, people who have problems do not like to face the fact that they have problems, and members of the family must seek help:

> *A 21-year-old woman began acting more and more strangely. Her husband tried to get her to see a psychotherapist, but she refused.*

As time passed, she began to neglect her obligations. She would miss several days' work in succession, sometimes not even telephoning her company to say that she would be absent. She stopped cleaning the house, and she neglected her appearance. She would spend the entire day in bed.

Eventually her husband found a psychotherapist who was willing to visit the woman at home. He made several visits, but the wife refused to speak to him.

Several days after his last visit, she attempted suicide with an overdose of sleeping pills. When her husband found her, she was difficult to arouse but still alive. An empty pill bottle was by the bedside.

The husband summoned an ambulance, and the wife was taken to an emergency room in a general hospital. When medically stable, she was transferred to a psychiatric hospital.

Sometimes, members of the family will not acknowledge or deal with a problem, and friends or acquaintances must intervene.

A 21-year-old man had behaved strangely for years, as his neighbors were painfully aware: he often was heard screaming late at night and had been caught burglarizing or vandalizing neighbors' homes.

His mother was afraid of him and of his threats, so she did not confront him about his actions and the desirability of treatment for his emotional problems. In fact, when he got into trouble with the law, she made excuses for him.

It was only after he had assaulted a neighbor that the police were called and he was finally referred to a psychiatric hospital.

Sometimes strangers are forced to intervene and arrange for treatment:

A 27-year-old man with a history of bizarre behavior took a loaded rifle and several handguns to a rooftop and began shooting at people in the street. The police barricaded the area and attempted to talk him into surrendering, but he responded only with gunfire.

As he ran across a roof, a marksman disabled him by shooting him in the leg. The police then disarmed him, and he was referred to a psychiatric hospital.

FINDING HELP

If you are faced with the problem of finding help for someone in your family, a good place to start is with your personal physician, who can judge whether psychiatric care is warranted and can refer you to a psychiatrist or other psychotherapist.

Sometimes people hesitate to discuss emotional problems with a family physician because they are embarrassed about admitting to such "weakness." Rest assured, emotional problems are no more a "weakness" than a broken arm or malfunctioning gallbladder. Physicians are well-equipped to address such problems.

> *A 57-year-old man had been seeing the same family physician for twenty-five years but was hesitant to reveal that his wife was having personal problems. He felt embarrassed in part because he did not feel a sense of personal closeness to the physician; their quarter-century of conversations, while friendly, had been confined to the patient's physical ailments.*
>
> *When he finally mustered the nerve to talk about the problem, he was astonished at how open and understanding the physician was and how helpful he was in recommending a psychotherapist.*

Another source of referral is a friend who has been helped by a psychotherapist.

> *A mother was concerned about her 17-year-old son, whose behavior had grown increasingly bizarre, but she did not know where to look for help. She remembered hearing about a friend who had seen a psychotherapist about marital problems. The mother hesitated to approach the woman, because she was afraid that she might be embarrassed or insulted.*
>
> *However, the friend turned out to be surprisingly open about the fact that she had undergone psychotherapy, and introduced the mother to her psychotherapist so that arrangements could be made for the son's treatment.*

Sometimes a lawyer can be a good source of a referral, especially if the lawyer's practice entails defending people who have been accused of crime. Some attorneys who specialize in criminal law work closely with psychiatrists and other psychotherapists.

A 19-year-old boy began showing a change in behavior after leaving home to enter college. Instead of actively participating in campus life, he acted strangely quiet and withdrawn, as if in a world of his own.

His father, uncertain of how to deal with the situation, took no action until the boy was arrested for vagrancy. The father then told the defense attorney that he believed that the boy was having emotional problems. The attorney referred the boy to a hospital for psychological evaluation.

Still another source of help is a privately-funded clinic or hospital that offers counseling for emotional problems.

A woman's 14-year-old daughter started having problems both at home and at school and began using drugs and alcohol. The woman had heard from friends how impressed they were with the caring attitude at a local private counseling center. She found the name of the counseling center in the phone book, and, because of the good reports, made an appointment for her daughter.

Yet another source of help might be a public facility for the emotionally troubled. For example, community mental health centers have been established throughout the United States and perform such services as at-home evaluation of psychiatric problems as well as outpatient therapy and referral to psychiatric hospitals. Other publicly-funded sources of help include mental health associations, suicide-prevention groups, and "hot line" services.

When his 23-year-old wife threatened to kill herself, a man telephoned a suicide-prevention center and was referred to a nearby community mental health center. He convinced his wife to accompany him there for crisis intervention therapy. She was given on-the-spot counseling and referred to a therapist for further treatment.

General hospitals and other public facilities, though not devoted exclusively or even principally to treatment of emotional problems, can also be helpful. City, county, and state hospitals are open twenty-four hours a day, and public health nurses often are available for at-home visits.

When their teen-aged son became violent after taking PCP, a street drug popular among some teenagers, his parents brought him to the emergency room of the county hospital, where he was evaluated medically, then referred for psychiatric evaluation. Because he had been using drugs for a long time, and because his acute state of disturbance did not ease within a reasonably short period, he was transferred to an acute care psychiatric hospital.

Still other public facilities or public-service agencies can be of assistance with emotional problems in certain categories. For example, childrens' protective services deal with problems involving child abuse, including mistreatment of children that may be wholly psychological (and, therefore, not involve beating or other physical abuse). Welfare agencies deal with many kinds of problems that relate to emotional disturbance within a family; certain staff members may be trained to recognize psychiatric problems and can help with referrals.

In an extreme emergency, the police are also available. However, few people who are emotionally disturbed are likely to want the police to get involved, and many emotionally disturbed people will manage to seem law-abiding and nonthreatening when the police are present.

When a 23-year-old woman began running around the house uncontrollably and threatening family members with a knife, her brother telephoned the police. When officers arrived, the woman insisted that there was no problem and that her brother was lying. She acted politely and seemed totally in control of herself.

Although the police may have believed that the brother would not have telephoned if the sister had not been behaving strangely, the behavior that they themselves observed did not in any way suggest that they should take action of any kind.

Fortunately for the family, the officers did not go directly to their squad car when they left the house. Instead, they waited for a few moments outside the closed door. Shortly after they had closed the door, the sister started laughing hysterically and boasting that now she would really get back at her family for calling the police.

She grabbed the kitchen-knife again and had started for the brother just as the police opened the door. She was promptly restrained and taken to a psychiatric hospital for evaluation.

It is very important for you to realize, as the relative of someone who is emotionally disturbed, that you cannot simply command that a person be taken into custody by the police and admitted to a psychiatric hospital. The days are long gone when a family can just "put someone away." Athough you may be convinced that your relative needs help, and although the police may agree with you, there are laws protecting the patient's rights.

A 27-year-old man with a long history of treatment for psychiatric problems had stopped taking his medication for only a short time before he began decompensating (that is, breaking down and deteriorating in his ability to function normally). He began talking aloud as if to visitors when his parents were the only people within earshot. He became verbally abusive and finally threatened to assault his parents.

Unable to persuade him to return to his psychiatrist, the parents summoned the police. When officers arrived, they found the young man in an agitated state. However, they felt he was sufficiently under control that he should not be taken to a hospital against his will.

The parents then sought an evaluation by the local mental health center. A team of psychotherapists came to the house and spoke to the young man and other members of the family.

Like the police, these psychotherapists concluded that the young man was not sufficiently out of control to warrant being hospitalized against his will. They suggested that the family's choices were either to adjust to the young man's behavior or put him out of the house. When the parents said they could not in good conscience turn the young man loose on the streets, the psychotherapists said, in effect, "Then you've just left yourself with only one option."

Sometimes, even though a person can be seen as desperately in need of *medical* treatment there may be legal barriers to involuntary hospitalization.

A 48-year-old man had been drinking steadily since becoming disabled in an accident at work ten years earlier. He suffered from cirrhosis of the liver, had suffered delirium tremens (the "DTs") twice, was diagnosed as requiring surgery for ulcers, and on several occasions had vomited blood.

He had lost a great deal of weight, was extremely pale, and often went for days at a time without shaving or bathing. When his wife demanded that he seek help or move out of their apartment, he borrowed money from his brother and rented a bed in a skid-row dormitory.

He lived in the dormitory for several months and continued to drink every day. Finally, he ran out of money and could not get anything more to drink. A few days later, he started getting shaky and began to hallucinate (to see things that did not exist).

When he complained to the manager that a group of tiny people had walked out from under his bed carrying an old shoe which spoke to him, the manager took him to a hospital. He repeated his story and was promptly admitted on an involuntary basis.

When he learned that he could not drink alcoholic beverages in the hospital and could not leave at will, he was angry and demanded to be released. He insisted that nothing was wrong with him, and he denied with special vehemence that he had a drinking problem.

Consistent with the law in the state where he lived, a court hearing was scheduled. The purpose of the hearing was to determine whether the patient should be released or whether someone could show cause that he should remain hospitalized against his will. His family argued that his health was deteriorating and that he would kill himself if someone did not intervene. He replied that he was perfectly capable of taking care of himself and that his relatives wanted to "railroad" him into the hospital because they were embarrassed by his idiosyncratic lifestyle.

The judge, impressed by the man's apparent coherence and articulateness (aided by his several days of sobriety while hospitalized), ordered him released. The man promptly resumed drinking heavily and continued to do so until, less than a year later, he died of liver failure.

DEALING WITH A RELATIVE'S RESISTANCE

Many people who are emotionally disturbed want desperately to be helped. Far from resisting the entreaties of relatives or friends that they seek treatment, they wish fervently that they had relatives or friends who could help them obtain treatment.

However, there are other people—and your relative may be among them—who resist the idea that they have problems. Indeed, the *visible* part of their problems—that is, the behavior that relatives or friends find troublesome—may be a defense against a deeper set of problems. Take away the defense and you force the person to face the original problems head-on, a confrontation that calls for more strength than a person may possess at the time.

Resistance is so common that behavioral scientists have classified the different styles that are the most commonly manifested. One of the most prevalent of these so-called defense mechanisms is "denial," where the person refuses to acknowledge that there is any problem at all:

> *A 51-year-old man had been drinking heavily for thirty-five years. When intoxicated, he would get into violent quarrels with his wife and sometimes would even threaten his children with a straight razor. On several occasions, according to his wife, he actually tried to kill the children.*
>
> *His wife begged him to seek professional help, and even his friends at work made comments about his drinking, but he denied that he had a problem. Even though he underwent several episodes of delirium tremens—the "DTs," involving hallucinations and violent trembling—he insisted that he drank only occasionally and could stop whenever he wished.*
>
> *It was only when he faced legal charges for driving while intoxicated that he entered treatment and finally acknowledged that he had a problem.*

Another of the defense mechanisms is "projection," where a person ascribes his or her thoughts and feelings to others.

> *A 24-year-old man, diagnosed as paranoid schizophrenic, had been in treatment for several years when he stopped taking medication because he decided that he did not need it. Within a few months he became unduly suspicious of people and began to develop the idea that his family was part of a conspiracy to kill him.*
>
> *He thought he was being watched all the time, but actually he was the one who was looking at others mistrustfully.*
>
> *He threatened people with violence—even strangers on the street—because he believed they were agents in the plot against him, but he never recognized his own provocative hostility.*
>
> *His family urged him to resume taking medication or to readmit himself to a hospital. His interpretation was that the family wanted to poison him with the medication, and if he allowed himself to get locked up, he would surely be killed.*
>
> *Eventually he was picked up by the police for attacking a stranger on the street. Taken to a psychiatric hospital, he insisted*

that his entire family was crazy but there was nothing wrong with him. In sum, because of the nature of his disorder, he "projected" onto others the thoughts and feelings he was having himself.

Yet another defense mechanism is "acting out," where a person obeys impulses instead of attempting to deal with them rationally.

> *A 22-year-old woman frequently talked about how unhappy her family was making her. She often said that she wished she were dead.*
>
> *Her boyfriend and her relatives tried to persuade her that she had a lot to live for and that she should not be entertaining thoughts of this kind. After an argument with her boyfriend, she took fifteen sleeping pills, locked herself into the bathroom, and refused to open the door. She had "acted out" her self-destructive impulses.*

Another common defense mechanism is "passive-aggressive behavior," where a person shows opposition by withholding cooperation without verbally challenging the ideas being opposed.

> *A 24-year-old housewife who had been depressed and nervous for years finally could no longer cope, but resisted her outpatient therapist's recommendation that she seek hospitalization. When finally he seemed to have persuaded her, she made appointments but did not keep them. Several times she claimed to have forgotten an appointment, and on several other occasions she insisted that her husband and the psychotherapist had erroneously scheduled the appointment for the wrong day.*
>
> *Finally, her husband scheduled the appointments for her and arranged to leave work early so that he could return to their home and drive her to the hospital. Three times in a row, he got home only to find that she was not ready to leave. She insisted that she could not go because she had household chores or shopping to do first. She "passively" resisted going to the hospital, but her "aggression" was expressed just the same.*

Yet another defense mechanism, "regression," involves a return to a more "primitive state of functioning," that is, a less mature stage of development in behavior.

> *A 19-year-old woman gradually withdrew from other people and began spending more and more time in her room. Eventually she refused to get out of bed and insisted that her mother bring her*

food, other necessities, and even a bedpan. She would not bathe herself, insisting that her mother do this for her. It was as if she had become a baby again.

As I have said, resistances of this sort are extremely common. Most people who are emotionally disturbed have a *stake* in behaving as they do. Although they might not consciously realize it, they may be hesitant to seek help for fear that they will be stripped of their defenses and forced to confront once again the psychological pain against which their present behavior is a reaction.

How can you, as a relative who seeks to help, deal with this situation? How can you convince someone about whom you care deeply to seek help?

The task will be difficult. The more advanced your relative's condition is, the more difficult the task is likely to be.

The best approach, I think, involves showing that you genuinely care and that you really want to help.

The specific steps that you take will depend not only on the problems you think your relative has but also on the resistances that your relative shows. Other considerations are how severe the problems are and how urgently treatment is needed. Yet another consideration is you—what kind of person you are and how your personality works.

I can't tell you exactly what to do to get your relative into treatment. Every case is so different that an attempt at offering general advice could be harmful rather than beneficial. However, I do believe that if you are really concerned, and if you use your best judgment, you will probably do the right thing.

What if, despite your best efforts, your relative still resists entering treatment? In that case, I believe it is best to consult a psychiatrist or other professional for advice. The professional can suggest the best approach for you based on your individual personality. Talking things over with a trained and objective observer can give you insights and help you work out a good plan.

If you prepare yourself, you can anticipate what objections and arguments you are likely to get from your relative, and you can figure out—in advance—how to answer them. You can also relieve yourself of some of your worries and feel stronger by the time you finally face the discussion. You might even find it helpful to go over the possible arguments in your mind, or rehearse by "role playing" or mentally acting out both parts of the conversation.

If you consult a professional about how to get help for your relative, you might also get a better picture of yourself and of how you fit into the situation. In other words, you might learn exactly why you want your relative to have help—and your motives may be more selfish than you realize.

For example, you may feel that your relative should be hospitalized because he or she cannot manage the tasks of everyday living. What you may discover is that you do not want the burden of having this troublesome person around.

Even though you may feel guilty, it is best to recognize your own feelings. In many cases, they may be legitimate; there are limitations to how much you—or anyone—can do for a relative, no matter how much love you feel.

In the process of sorting out these issues, you might unexpectedly learn that you can benefit from some self-examination.

A case in point:

A 38-year-old housewife was upset about her husband's chronic drinking. He never seemed to have time for her or their children. He was bad company, easily irritated, and quick to anger. When she tried to talk to him about their problems, he either would refuse quietly to discuss the matter or he would go into a rage.

Convinced that he would never agree to see a psychotherapist, she consulted one on her own. She said that she did not want treatment for herself but hoped that if she began she could somehow persuade her husband to join later.

While discussing how to get him into treatment, she acknowledged that he probably would not acquiesce unless she threatened to leave him and take the children with her. Moreover, she said, he would have to believe that she was really willing to do this, for she had made threats in the past and had not followed through on them.

This opened up an interesting area of study. The woman had to recognize her own problem—namely, that she was unwilling to stand up for herself, and that she would have to do so before she could expect her husband to change his behavior.

This led to another discovery: the woman was actually a "co-alcoholic," "enabling" him to continue his drinking by calling work to say he was "sick" when he was really hung over, making excuses to the children for his intolerable behavior, making light of it to friends, and actually buying alcohol for him when he pleaded desperately enough. Because of her own problems, which included a "need to be needed," she did not want to admit that her husband's behavior—and her own—was really unacceptable and not at all what she wanted for herself and her family.

Once she faced up to this, she was able to give her husband an ultimatum and mean it. Her husband recognized this, and, rather than lose her and the children, went into treatment and stopped drinking.

Psychological resistances are not the only sort of difficulty you might encounter in getting your relative to seek treatment in a psychiatric hospital. Realistic concerns about the ramifications of hospitalization may also be a deterrent. For example, because of the stigma attached to mental illness, a person may fear loss of a job or of status within the community.

However, despite such difficulties, you can be of great help if your relative requires hospitalization. If you have any question about how to deal with the situation, get the advice of a psychiatrist or another mental health professional who is familiar with such problems and can address the specifics of your relative's case. In this way, you can help your relative get needed treatment as soon as possible—and contribute greatly to your relative's speedy recovery.

3

Arranging Hospitalization

You may have thought that your involvement ends once a psychiatrist or someone else in authority has made the decision to hospitalize your relative. This is not so. Your help may be needed even more once plans for hospitalization have begun.

If a person is going to be admitted to a psychiatric hospital—or to any other kind of hospital—there is not much opportunity to practice consumerism. If you have a good insurance policy and/or a great deal of money, you might be able to choose among private hospitals. If you have neither money nor psychiatric insurance, you usually will go to a county, state, or Veterans Administration (VA) hospital. Whatever the situation, the patient and the patient's family will be expected to follow the hospital's normal procedures.

This is not to say that you do not have certain legal rights. My point is that the best way to ensure that your relative will receive the best treatment with a minimum of administrative or other delay is to recognize the situation for what it is and to make it as easy as possible for the people who are in charge to make it as easy as possible for you.

BEFORE GOING TO THE HOSPITAL

By reading this book, you are doing one of the most important things you can to ensure that everything will go well for your relative: you are learning about what hospitalization entails and how you can help. The general background information will give you helpful preparation even if it does not exactly describe the specifics of your relative's case. If after reading the book you have questions about the hospital or its procedures or what your relative's treatment will involve, discuss them with the psychiatrist or other members of the hospital's staff.

A major part of the admission procedure in a psychiatric hospital, as in any other hospital, is making financial arrangements.

If the patient is being admitted to a Veterans Administration hospital or some other publicly-funded facility, payment usually will be arranged through the government (federal, state, or local), but you may still be responsible for part of the bill. In addition, someone may have to obtain the documentation required by the paying organization to prove that the patient is eligible.

For example, if the patient is a veteran, you may have to provide information about the patient's military service. In certain localities, you may be required to provide proof of residency to obtain admission to a state or county hospital. For some facilities, quite a bit of additional information and/or documentation may be required.

Whatever the requirements, it is wise to learn them as early as possible so that you will have as much time as possible to comply with them. For example, if you are going to apply for admission to a VA facility, it would be wise to telephone the nearest VA office for information rather than simply showing up at the VA hospital and asking for help. A telephone call can save you many unnecessary steps if you learn what documentation is required and then assemble it before going to the hospital.

If you are arranging admission to a private hospital, it is important to know if the patient has insurance that covers psychiatric hospitalization. If there is psychiatric coverage, what types of treatment are covered?

For example, does the coverage include drug and alcohol problems? Are only certain categories of hospitals covered; for example, those accredited by certain organizations, such as the Joint Commission on Accreditation of Hospitals? How long a stay does the policy cover? Is there a limited dollar amount? Is that amount allocated "per confinement" (that is, for each period of hospitalization), "per calendar year," or over an entire lifetime?

If there are several insurance policies, how do they work in combination? For example, does one policy cover whatever treatments a second policy excludes, or do both policies cover the same basic treatments and exclude all others? It is important to understand these matters at the very start so that there will be no unpleasant surprises later about large bills that are not covered by insurance.

Ideally, of course, you would be able to anticipate far in advance what demands would be made on your insurance coverage and you would arrange a policy or a combination of policies that provided everything that is needed. However, chances are that when you bought the insurance you had little if any idea of the problems that might arise. Accordingly, you may have a policy that offers very little or no psychiatric coverage.

Whatever the coverage, you should know what it is before arranging hospitalization. If the language of the policy confuses you, discuss the policy with your insurance agent. If you have a company-provided group policy, discuss the coverage with the appropriate officer at your place of work.

If insurance provides only partial coverage (or no coverage) the hospital may require a deposit before the patient is accepted. The deposit may involve more money than most people can raise on short notice. Therefore, it is very important to know—well in advance of admission—exactly what the hospital will require.

It is also a good idea to learn—before the patient is admitted—as much as you can about the hospital's procedures. For example, what are the policies regarding visitors? Are patients permitted to leave the hospital periodically to spend time with their families at home? What kinds of recreational facilities are available to patients? May families or other visitors bring gifts? May patients have their own radios or television sets?

Your choice of a hospital, if you have a choice, normally will not depend on such peripheral considerations. It is much more important to find the hospital which can provide the best treatment for the particular problem your relative has. However, if you feel that all other factors are equal, you might very well choose one hospital over another because its policies offer you greater convenience or offer the patient greater comfort. The more you learn about the hospital's procedures before you apply for admission, the better equipped you will be to make a decision. Some hospitals offer brochures or other descriptive material that will assist you in making comparisons.

WHAT TO EXPECT
AT THE ADMISSIONS OFFICE

If you were ever admitted as a medical or surgical patient at a general hospital—or even just had to go to an emergency room—you know that the admission procedure can be complicated and time-consuming. The procedure in psychiatric hospitals is at least equally complicated and time-consuming, even if the patient volunteers for treatment. When hospitalization is involuntary, the complications and time can increase commensurately.

To someone who is not familiar with hospitals, many of the procedures may seem unnecessary or unduly burdensome. In fact, each procedure exists for a reason. Some procedures are required by the governmental agencies that license hospitals. Others are required by insurance companies. Still others were developed by the hospital to facilitate the handling of the patient's records. Although you may feel angry at having to deal with all the paperwork, try to remember that it is designed to help in securing the best possible treatment for your relative.

If a patient is entering the hospital voluntarily, he or she will be required to fill out certain forms that are similar to those used at general hospitals. They are designed to elicit such information as the patient's home address, telephone number, employer, and next of kin. Still other forms solicit financial information—for example, how payment will be made and by whom. If the patient has psychiatric insurance, you should bring a copy of the insurance card to the hospital. You should also have the name, address, and phone number of the insurance agent or claims office, so that you can ask for whatever additional information the hospital may require.

At the admissions office, a patient signs a comprehensive document to authorize general treatment at the hospital. Later, after evaluation by a psychiatrist and other staff, the patient may be asked to sign additional documents authorizing specific medications or special procedures. These so-called informed consent forms are much like the documents a prospective surgical patient signs before surgery is performed. In essence, the patient gives permission to the hospital and its staff to perform certain procedures. The patient also acknowledges that the treatment involves certain risks but states that the risks are undertaken voluntarily because the patient has judged that the potential benefits outweigh the risks.

In certain cases, a court may have appointed a relative as the patient's conservator or guardian. In that situation, the relative may be called on to consider the treatment that the psychiatrist has planned and to give consent on the patient's behalf. If you are asked to give such consent, and if you have any question whatever regarding the proposed treatment, discuss it with the psychiatrist. Do not give your consent unless you are fully satisfied that the risks of the treatment are outweighed by the potential benefits.

In recent years there has been considerable opposition to involuntary psychiatric hospitalization. Organizations that advocate "patients' rights" have brought lawsuits around the country trying to ensure that patients have as little involuntary treatment as possible.

Many psychiatrists and other mental health professionals feel that the patients'-rights movement may ultimately hurt many people who need psychiatric help. However, most jurisdictions have laws that strictly limit the circumstances under which people may be hospitalized (or otherwise treated) against their will. Because of these laws, you may sometimes find psychiatrists or psychiatric hospitals reluctant to admit a relative whom you regard as desperately in need of help. In some situations, the psychiatrist or other officials of the hospital may agree with you that help is desperately needed, but they will refuse to admit the patient because they believe that they cannot do so without infringing on the patient's legal rights.

Generally, when society judges a person's behavior to be dangerous or otherwise unacceptable, laws provide for involuntary treatment. Although laws vary substantially from state to state, they are alike in that they apply to people who seem to be dangerous to themselves or others or so gravely disabled that they are unable to care for themselves satisfactorily (for example, in senility).

Most such laws make a distinction between "initial evaluation and treatment" and more extended care, and it is often easier to arrange the former than the latter.

An involuntary stay for initial evaluation and treatment usually lasts for no more than a few days. The patient is observed in a controlled setting and may also be given medications. This brief period of hospitalization allows enough time for a psychiatrist to judge whether inpatient treatment should be continued or whether the patient has recovered sufficiently to be discharged.

Although an extremely brief period of involuntary hospitalization may make sense to many people—and especially to the concerned relatives of a patient who seems dangerous—not everyone agrees that the procedure should be permitted. Patients themselves may be especially vehement in opposing the procedure, although they may later agree that it was beneficial. A case in point:

> A 19-year-old woman had a quarrel with her boyfriend, who said he was going to leave her. Despondent, she swallowed virtually every pill she could find in her house—aspirin, sleeping pills, tranquilizers, even her father's medication for ulcers.
>
> She quickly began to feel strange and realized that she had acted rashly and foolishly. Alone in the house, she tried to telephone her parents, who were visiting relatives. The line was busy. She started to dial the operator for emergency assistance but passed out before she could complete the call.
>
> Fortunately, her parents returned an hour later, saw the empty pill bottles, and summoned an ambulance. At the emergency room of a general hospital, the daughter was given medication to make her vomit. She then was interviewed by a psychiatrist, who ordered that she be admitted to the county psychiatric hospital for several days' observation and additional interviewing.
>
> She was still drowsy when she went to the psychiatric hospital, and, as soon as she was taken to a ward, she fell asleep. When she awoke twelve hours later, she was both astonished and furious to find herself in a ward with what she described as "a lot of crazy people." She demanded that she be released.
>
> Her mother was summoned. The daughter, acknowledging that she had behaved unwisely when she swallowed all those pills, insisted that she did not belong in the hospital because she was not "crazy." She argued that she had suffered enough and that she now was being punished for her unwise behavior. The mother, seeing that many patients in the ward were visibly quite disturbed, sympathized with the daughter and asked the psychiatrist to release her.
>
> The psychiatrist acknowledged that the young woman did not have the same kind of problem as many of the people the mother had seen on the ward. However, he pointed out, her self-destructive behavior obviously was emotionally based and had to be taken seriously. The locked ward provided an environment in which the girl's safety could be ensured.
>
> The mother insisted that the daughter be released. The psychiatrist refused to discharge her. That evening, the daughter

tried again to commit suicide by fashioning a noose from a bedsheet. Had she not been in the hospital, her attempt at self-destruction might have been successful.

Now supported fully by the girl's family, the psychiatrist undertook crisis intervention psychotherapy. The girl was encouraged to speak with members of her family, all of whom expressed love for her. Her boyfriend was persuaded to come to the hospital, and his appearance cheered the young woman greatly.

After several days, she was discharged to outpatient therapy with a psychiatrist in her own community. After six months, she was described as making satisfactory progress.

If it seems after a brief period of evaluation that an involuntary patient requires additional treatment, such treatment can be arranged. However, the patient may have a hearing before a judge. Lawyers, usually from the public defender's office, take an active role in protecting the personal rights of the patient. Frequently the courts will order a person discharged, even though psychiatrists may testify that treatment is desirable. Rarely will a court order continued hospitalization if the patient is not seen to be dangerous or seriously disabled.

Here are two case histories, one in which the patient was discharged, the other in which involuntary hospitalization was continued:

A 77-year-old widow showed signs of age-related mental deterioration. Confused and forgetful, she neglected the basic tasks of caring for herself. She sometimes went for several days without eating, and on several occasions she became lost while away from her apartment and could not find her way back home.

Her only son, who lived several hundred miles away, tried to persuade her to move in with him and his family. She refused, saying that she did not want to be a burden to them and also that she did not want to leave the city where she had spent most of her life. Since the son was unable to persuade her to move, he arranged for her to be hospitalized for several days' tests that could reveal whether her mental malfunctioning might be a result of senile dementia, which is more or less untreatable, or of some other medical problem with a better prognosis.

The son brought his mother to the hospital, but she refused to sign herself in. She was placed on an "involuntary hold." At her request, an attorney from the public defender's office represented her at a hearing. A judge ruled that confinement was justified.

After several days, the psychiatrist determined that drugs could bring about some improvement in the woman's condition. She was discharged in the custody of her son and went to live with him and his family.

A 29-year-old man with a history of chronic schizophrenia had been functioning fairly well, but gradually his condition deteriorated. He had wanted to remain at home under the care of his parents, but they felt that they could not deal with his erratic behavior. Finally they convinced him to accompany them to the emergency room of the county hospital. After evaluation, he was admitted to the psychiatric ward as an involuntary patient.

Treated for several days with antipsychotic medications, he showed little improvement. The psychiatrist decided that a longer period of hospitalization was desirable, but the patient disagreed and demanded a court hearing.

His parents and the psychiatrist testified that he was too disorganized to take care of himself. They stated that in the past he had spent his disability checks foolishly within a few days of getting them and was left with no money for food, clothing, or shelter. They pointed out that he had a history of defaulting on his rent. They argued that if he were not hospitalized he very well might blunder his way into a dangerous situation.

The patient replied that he was able to provide for his basic needs with a disability check that was due to arrive that very day. He added that he could manage his life well without his parents' help and that he had come to the hospital only because they had urged him to do so. His lawyer argued that while his history might seem strange to many people, no one had provided evidence that the patient was unable to take care of himself, much less that he was guilty of any crime that might warrant incarceration.

The judge ordered the patient discharged, but he was readmitted several days later after the police picked him up for disturbing the peace.

Although decisions of courts in cases like these may be frustrating to relatives of patients, it is the task of the court to ensure that patients' rights are not violated, not to ensure that patients receive the best possible treatment. This difference in viewpoint is often difficult for concerned relatives to understand and accept, because they are convinced that the patient would benefit from treatment. However, as long as our laws regarding involuntary hospitalization remain as they are, the likelihood is that courts will release a great many people whom relatives and psychiatrists believe need additional treatment.

Protection of patients' rights includes protection from "preventive detention"—that is, incarceration to ensure that a threatened act will not be committed. Even though a person may threaten violence—up to and including assault or even murder—the threat may be regarded as not sufficient to justify psychiatric confinement. The position of the courts generally is that intervention is not warranted unless there is a likelihood that the act will be committed.

Ironically, if a person is freed from involuntary psychiatric hospitalization under these circumstances and then goes on to commit murder or some other crime, the person may escape punishment by claiming "diminished capacity." In other words, the court may rule that the person cannot be held fully accountable for the crime because he or she did not know fully what he or she was doing.

Although this may be frustrating for all of us, we must operate within the system as it now stands. Therefore, in dealing with relatives who have psychiatric problems, the best course of action generally is to persuade a person that help should be sought. Only after all avenues of persuasion have been exhausted should involuntary hospitalization be pursued.

Ultimately, of course, the most important reason that treatment be voluntary has nothing to do with the law. The patient's desire for treatment is important from the standpoint of psychotherapy. If patients themselves make the decision to get help, treatment is much more likely to be successful.

4

How A Patient Is Evaluated
At A Psychiatric Hospital

What will happen once your relative has been admitted to a psychiatric hospital? Fundamentally, two things:

(1) The patient will be evaluated;

(2) The patient will be treated.

If this sounds much like what happens in a general hospital, you should not be surprised, because psychiatric hospitals and general hospitals operate in much the same way. In fact, both have a great deal in common with a wide variety of other enterprises that specialize in solving one sort of problem or another.

In psychiatric hospitals as in general hospitals, evaluation of a patient may begin before admission. For example, if you consulted a gastroenterologist about abdominal pain, you may have been diagnosed as having gallstones and admitted to the hospital specifically for the purpose of having these stones removed surgically. If you were in outpatient psychotherapy with a psychiatrist, you might have been diagnosed as having depression so severe that you could best be treated in a hospital. In either situation, there might be additional tests or other evaluative procedures once you entered the hospital, but, by and large, the evaluation has been made and you are ready to begin treatment.

In other situations, a person will not have been under a doctor's care before being admitted. For example, if you were walking down the street and suddenly had an attack of chest pain, you might be rushed in an ambulance to a general hospital, where your case would be evaluated by the emergency room staff. If the police found you wandering naked and confused on a busy street, you might be taken to a psychiatric hospital for evaluation.

Evaluation in a psychiatric hospital actually begins when the first contact is made, even if the contact involves only a telephone call to ask questions or make arrangements for admission. The person who makes contact may be the prospective patient, a relative or friend, an outpatient therapist, a public agency, an emergency room in another hospital, the police, or some other source. The person at the hospital with whom contact is made will be a nurse or some other member of the staff, who will interview the caller briefly about what sort of treatment is being sought.

This first phase of evaluation is not usually very detailed. One of its main purposes is determining that the hospital is an appropriate place for the prospective patient to be treated. For example, some hospitals do not admit teenagers. In this situation, the caller would be referred to another hospital. Or the caller might be someone who is emotionally disturbed but does not require emergency treatment and has not consulted anyone about the problem; in this situation, the interviewer might refer the person to a psychotherapist.

If the hospital is an appropriate place for the treatment that is being sought, the interviewer may take notes about the prospective patient's situation so that preparations can be made for arrival. For example, a bed must be reserved. A person who is suicidal, violent, or confused will be assigned to a locked ward where he or she will be under constant observation, while most other patients will be placed in unlocked wards and not observed so closely.

Once this preliminary evaluation has been accomplished, the hospital will be ready to admit the patient. The next phase of evaluation—"intake" by the nursing staff—will occur soon, but first there are administrative procedures to be performed. They include the logging of personal information and the arrangements for payment that were discussed in the previous chapter.

Most patients will be able to participate in the admission procedures, but severely disturbed patients may be sent directly to a locked ward. In this situation, relatives or friends—or the police, or whoever else may have helped arrange the admission—will have to attend to these details.

When admission procedures have been completed, there usually will be a brief orientation for the patient and any relatives or friends who may have accompanied him or her. You will probably be given an overview of the hospital's layout and procedures. Also, you most likely will be told when the patient can expect to see a psychiatrist and when there will be an opportunity for you to discuss the psychiatrist's findings. You probably will be briefed on certain of the hospital's procedures; for example, deposits might be required for locker keys or similar items, and you might be advised to take home any jewelry or other valuables that the patient may be carrying and leave only a small amount of money for personal use at a gift shop, in soft-drink machines, et cetera.

In most hospitals, this orientation will be rather general and will not deal with such questions as clothing, patients' activities, and the like. These subjects normally are addressed in the nursing staff intake, which comes next.

NURSING STAFF INTAKE

The term "nursing staff" comprises not only traditional nurses (registered nurses, or R.N.'s) but also other trained personnel such as psychiatric technicians, mental health aides, and people with other psychiatry-related degrees. The intake, or admission procedure, involves situating the patient in the hospital and starting diagnosis and treatment.

An orientation is also part of the admission procedure. If family and friends have accompanied the patient, they normally will be invited to attend. One member of the staff generally will discuss the hospital's program, physical layout, and rules. Information will be provided about the various therapy programs (psychotherapy, occupational therapy, art therapy, et cetera) and the scheduling of meals and visiting hours. Restrictions, such as special areas for smoking or rules about matches and cigarette lighters, will be explained.

During this period, the nursing staff will assess how much control the patient has over his or her behavior. Some patients will seem totally under control and completely cooperative, while others may be perceived as rebellious or even dangerous and requiring physical restraint. If a person seems to be in control of his or her behavior, the nursing staff must take into account the possibility that he or she may suddenly attempt suicide, commit assault, try to escape, or perhaps set a fire. Someone on the nursing staff must assess how carefully the patient should be watched. If there is any fear that the patient may behave dangerously, the patient's movement and privileges must be restricted.

An important duty of the nursing staff during intake is to make certain that the patient has not brought any dangerous objects into the hospital. Guns, knives, and other weapons obviously belong in this category. So do many other articles that most people think of as innocuous. For example, such toilet articles as mirrors or glass containers might be dangerous to a person who is suicidal. Jewelry, money, and other valuables might be placed in a safe rather than being allowed in a ward where other patients might try to steal them.

Sharp or heavy objects may be taken away if there is any fear that they might be used as weapons. For example, an elderly patient might be accustomed to walking with a wooden cane. The cane would not be dangerous if the patient was the only person who used it; however, some other patient could put it to violent use. So the nursing staff might replace it with a lightweight aluminum walker.

Clothing will be evaluated for its potential danger, as will such objects as curling irons and other electrical appliances. The nursing staff will want to be sure that they are not defective—for example, because of faulty wiring, which could cause a fire. The staff also will want to be certain that the patient can handle these appliances responsibly and not risk injury with them.

The staff usually will not allow tape recorders, cameras, and other devices that might invade the privacy or violate the confidentiality of other patients. Also, of course, the staff will confiscate liquor, drugs, and other intoxicants.

The patient's physical and psychiatric history will be taken. Important parts of the psychiatric history include events leading to hospitalization as well as the patient's record of treatment as an inpatient or outpatient. The nursing staff will also seek information about the patient's familial relationships and current living situation. Important parts of the physical history include allergies, a record of surgery and major illnesses, and a complete list of medications that the patient may now be taking or may have taken recently.

Many patients will be using medication when they enter the

hospital, and some patients will bring that medication with them. Medications may include not only psychoactive drugs, such as antidepressants or tranquilizers, but also pills for high blood pressure, digestive problems, or a host of other maladies.

No matter how innocuous a medication may seem to you, the nursing staff probably will take it away. There are several reasons for this. First, medications react with each other, and it is extremely important for anyone who prescribes medications to control what is being taken and under which circumstances; it could be extremely dangerous for a psychiatrist to prescribe certain medications without knowing that the patient is taking other medications. Second, the hospital wants to ensure that the patient is taking all necessary medications on schedule; thus, a log will be established for the patient's medications, and the staff will supervise the administration of these medications. Third, there is the possibility that certain patients might take an overdose, whether simply through inattention or confusion, or in an attempt at suicide, or to provoke some physical reaction that might lead to transfer to a general hospital. Fourth, there is always the possibility that some other patient might gain possession of a medication and put it to a dangerous use.

In the course of gathering all this information, the nursing staff will evaluate the patient's appearance and demeanor. Is the patient unkempt and apparently unconcerned about appearance? Does the patient seem agitated, drowsy, restless, withdrawn, hyperactive, lethargic, or unable to concentrate? These factors may be of clinical significance, and they also will be useful as points of comparison as treatment progresses.

The staff will also observe relationships between the patient and any relatives or friends who may have accompanied him or her to the hospital. How well do they get along? How helpful and supportive are relatives and friends? The staff, seeking as complete and objective a picture of the patient as possible, will want to see the patient from the point of view of relatives and friends. What do they think of the patient? What do they believe are the reasons for the patient's problems? What is their opinion of how and why the patient came to the hospital?

This interaction between the nursing staff and the patient's relatives and friends normally will continue during the entire time that the patient is hospitalized. The staff will try to gain a better understanding of what led to the patient's problem and also will seek information that will be helpful when plans are being made to discharge the patient.

The staff will be attentive to whether the patient seems to feel better after a visit or seems more upset than before the visitor arrived. If the patient becomes more disturbed for any reason (or if visitors are disruptive or disturbing to the patient), visitors may be asked to change their behavior or leave the hospital.

A major obligation of the nursing staff at intake is to write a "care plan" for the patient. The patient's physical state will be evaluated, and special problems will be addressed. For example, does an elderly patient require assistance in moving about? Does a patient have a problem with constipation or incontinence? Can the patient attend without assistance to such self-care as bathing, grooming, and dressing in clean clothing? If a patient is extremely lethargic (drowsy, sleepy) or agitated, special attention may be necessary. A withdrawn patient may require assistance in socializing, while an intrusive patient may need redirection.

PSYCHIATRIC EVALUATION

When the nursing-staff intake is complete, the patient will be interviewed by the psychiatrist who will be in charge of the case.

In some instances, the psychiatrist will already know the patient. They may have worked together in outpatient psychother-apy, and the psychiatrist may have arranged for admission to the hospital. When this is the case, the psychiatrist usually will already have made his evaluation and probably also his diagnosis, so it will be possible to begin treatment immediately.

In other instances, the psychiatrist will not have seen the patient before—for example, if the patient simply appeared at the hospital asking for help or was referred from the emergency room at a general hospital or after an encounter with the police. In these cases, the psychiatrist will have to work quite a bit harder at developing information about the patient, especially if the patient is resisting hospitalization.

After the psychiatrist has taken the patient's medical and psychiatric history, he or she will write a report. This report will then be consulted regularly as the psychiatrist and other members of the staff continue to work with the patient. A complete report also allows, if necessary, the taking over of the case by another psychiatrist, who will be able to proceed without going back to the very beginning.

As in all of medicine, there is a fairly standard approach to organizing the information about a patient, although there are some variations from hospital to hospital and from doctor to doctor. Ideally, the work-up will be as detailed and as comprehensive as possible, but, in practice, there may not be time to perform an exhaustive evaluation. To obtain even a sketchy history of a person's life may require a great many hours. At present, with the typical short hospital stay, psychiatrists rarely have time to explore a patient's history fully. Instead, they must focus on only the most pertinent aspects, seeking information that will permit the patient to be treated as quickly and effectively as possible.

Below I will list some of the subject areas a psychiatrist would explore in a lengthy evaluation. Your relative's psychiatrist almost certainly will not explore all of them, for some will be irrelevant to the patient's circumstances and others will be of such little probable value that the psychiatrist will feel the time would be better spent on other matters. However, the patient—or you, if the patient is uncommunicative—should be prepared to answer questions in all of the subject areas.

Psychiatric History

IDENTIFICATION: The report starts, as might be expected, with the name of the patient and certain identifying characteristics. Ordinarily information will include age, marital status, gender, occupation, and previous admissions—if any—to this hospital.

CHIEF COMPLAINT: Why did the patient come to the hospital? What was he or she feeling that persuaded him or her to seek help, or what behavior by the patient persuaded someone else to intervene? The psychiatrist normally will try to get this information in the patient's own words, even if the patient was hospitalized involuntarily. However, if the patient cannot or will not provide this account, the psychiatrist will obtain a description from the referring emergency room or other agency.

HISTORY OF PRESENT ILLNESS: What was the development of the problem for which the patient is being hospitalized? What was the patient like before the problem arose? What changes did the patient or other people notice as the problem started and then got worse?

It is important to itemize any treatments the patient may have undergone for the problem, including psychotherapy, medications, and previous hospitalizations, with dates and results. This information can be helpful when the psychiatrist is assessing how severe the patient's problem is and what the likely future course of the condition will be.

HISTORY OF OTHER PSYCHIATRIC PROBLEMS: What other problems, if any, has the patient had? When did they first arise? How long did they last?

Once again, it is important to itemize treatments, including psychotherapy, medications, and previous hospitalizations, with dates and results.

PERSONAL, MEDICAL, AND FAMILY HISTORIES AND CURRENT SOCIAL SITUATION: Now the psychiatrist goes beyond any account of emotional difficulties and elicits the patient's account of his or her entire life, with special emphasis on medical conditions and personal relationships, for both of these can have particular bearing on psychiatric problems.

The amount of information that the psychiatrist seeks will be determined by the circumstances of the interview and the purposes of hospitalization. The information could include details about history of mental illness in the family and whether the patient was a planned and wanted child. Were there problems during childhood, such as temper tantrums? How well did the patient adjust to school? Is there a history of special problems, such as a learning disability? During adolescence, did the patient have many friends or only a few? How close were the relationships? Does the patient smoke or abuse alcohol or drugs? What is the history of his or her use of these agents? How did the patient learn about sex? What is the history of sexual experiences and relationships with other people? Is the patient married? Are there problems? What kind? What types of work has the patient done? How many jobs has he or she had, and for how long?

The psychiatrist will also seek information about the patient's current living arrangements. Is money a major problem? Will the patient, by being hospitalized, lose a job or a place to live? If the patient has children, who will take care of them while the patient is in the hospital?

Because an initial assessment must often be made rapidly so that emergency treatment can begin, the psychiatrist may ask only a few questions about many of these subjects. Additional information, if it is needed, can be obtained later, as treatment progresses. Obviously, some matters, such as the history of a disease that may affect the brain, will be more important than certain details of the patient's childhood, and the psychiatrist will exercise judgment about which subjects to address at what level.

Examination of Mental Status

This next step in the psychiatric evaluation is the equivalent of a physical examination during a medical evaluation. Just as an internist systematically examines the body of a patient who suffers abdominal pain, the psychiatrist systematically examines the mind of a person who evidences psychological pain.

Actually, the examination of the patient's mental status began when the interview began, for everything that the psychiatrist observed and heard was revealing in one way or another about the patient's mental state. For example, the patient's ability to express ideas reveals some things about his or her intelligence as well as about his or her self-control.

However, the psychiatrist will not simply form general impressions about these matters. He or she will systematically note observations and impressions that derive from what has transpired in the interview and will ask additional questions to develop information about matters that require amplification or clarification.

Here is a sort of checklist of some things the psychiatrist is observing:

First, the examiner notes the patient's general appearance. Facial expression, posture, grooming, and clothing all can be revealing of the patient's mental condition. Does the patient look healthy or sickly? Does the patient seem angry, frightened, apathetic, perplexed, contemptuous, ill-at-ease, poised? Does the patient exhibit such signs of anxiety as restlessness or a tense posture? Are there shifts in the level of anxiety during the interview?

What is the patient's behavior like? Does he or she exhibit twitches, mannerisms, or unusual gestures? Does he or she seem agitated, combative, hyperactive, retarded, rigid?

Does the patient speak unusually rapidly or slowly? Is the speech unusually loud, monotonous, slurred, mumbled, hesitant, whispered? Does the patient talk in a spontaneous manner?

How does the patient relate to the examiner? Is the patient's attitude cooperative, hostile, attentive, ingratiating, frank, seductive, guarded, evasive, defensive?

What are the patient's thought processes like? Is the thinking coherent, or do thoughts seem to wander in a confused way? Does the patient express an overabundance of ideas and seem unable to connect them? Does the patient answer questions directly, or does he or she seem evasive or uncomprehending? Are replies goal-directed? Are they relevant to what was asked? Are cause-effect relationships lacking? Are statements illogical, rambling, tangential?

What is the patient's mood and "affect"—that is, expression of feelings? How does the patient say he or she feels? How does this compare with what the psychiatrist observes? Does the patient seem depressed, despairing, anxious, irritable, angry, terrified, expansive, euphoric, awed, self-contemptuous? What is the amount and range of expression? Does the patient display an evenness of mood, or have there been broad fluctuations during the interview? Is the patient's emotional expression appropriate to the subject under discussion? (If, for example, a person laughs while describing a tragedy, the emotion can be regarded as inappropriate and perhaps evidence of emotional disturbance.)

Also important is the thought content. Are there strange or paranoid ideas? Does the patient have delusions? (For example, does he or she claim to be a religious figure?) If there are delusions, how tightly are they organized? (For example, if a patient claims to be the object of conspirators, is the conspiracy described logically with every element seemingly in place, or does the patient merely complain vaguely of some people who are "after him or her" without any apparent purpose?) Does the patient hear voices or have visions? If so, what does he or she see or hear? How often? Is the patient preoccupied about suicide or homicide?

Another area of evaluation involves the patient's degree of alertness, intellectual functioning, and awareness. (For example, the presence of sedation by drugs can be important, as can effects of physical illness.)

Orientation is assessed. How well-connected is the patient to time, place, and circumstance? Does the patient know today's date and the approximate time of day? Does he or she know that the interview is taking place in a hospital? Does he or she know approximately how long he or she has been there?

How intelligent is the patient? How good is the fund of information that he or she possesses? Is there any impairment in abstract thinking ability? (For example, can the patient recognize similarities and differences? Can he or she interpret proverbs?)

Memory is evaluated. Are there noteworthy gaps in the patient's memory? Can he or she remember distant events but not recent ones? Can he or she remember the names of close friends? Are certain types of memories blocked—for example, events during a certain period in life, or events relating to a certain person? Can the patient perform certain simple memory exercises—for example, repeating six digits after the psychiatrist dictates them?

Can the patient concentrate? (For example, how well can the patient perform simple arithmetical calculations?)

Has the patient demonstrated the inability to control aggressive or sexual impulses? (For example, has he or she recently struck someone, been verbally abusive, or committed sexual assault?)

Does the patient show good judgment? Is the patient able to understand the likely outcome of certain behavior—for example, that jumping out a third-story window could result in injury or death? Understanding such relationships, does the patient avoid such behavior?

How much insight does the patient have? Does the patient have awareness of his or her present condition? Does the patient remember acts or feelings that led to his or her hospitalization and connect those acts or feelings with being hospitalized? Is the patient aware of his or her own motives?

In the opinion of the psychiatrist, how reliable is the patient's account of all that has happened? If the patient is not telling the truth, is it because he or she is deliberately lying or because he or she cannot differentiate between truth and falsehood? (The psychiatrist's judgment will be based not only on an overall impression of the patient's mental competence, as developed thus far in the evaluation, but also on a comparison of what the patient has said and what is known from other sources—for example, police reports, the account of a psychotherapist who has referred the patient, or the accounts of the patient's family and friends.)

When the psychiatrist has completed this examination of the patient's mental status, he or she may feel ready to make a diagnosis and plan the patient's treatment. In a great many instances, the psychiatrist will have made a tentative diagnosis rather early in the examination and will have continued with the examination mainly to test that tentative diagnosis or to determine if there are still other elements present in the case. However, in other instances, the psychiatrist may feel that further studies are necessary before a diagnosis can be made.

Further Diagnostic Studies

They may include a physical examination, specialized medical tests (for example, an electroencephalogram, which tests the functioning of the brain), certain psychological tests, interviews with the patient's family or friends (either by the psychiatrist or by a social worker or other staff member), and additional psychiatric diagnostic interviews with the patient (either by the psychiatrist or by a colleague, perhaps one who specializes in a certain type of disorder).

PHYSICAL EXAMINATION: A physical examination is performed on every hospitalized patient, and screening tests such as blood tests, urinalysis, and chest x-ray are often routine.

The findings of a physical examination can help explain a great deal about a psychiatric patient's condition, and even discover unsuspected medical illnesses. Psychological and medical problems often are connected, and many psychiatric conditions can be traced to biological causes. When such is the case, elimination of the biological cause results in dramatic improvement, although there may still be other problems that developed independently of the biological problem.

The task of determining whether or not medical illness is causing psychiatric symptoms can be very complicated. If the psychiatrist suspects a particular medical problem, he or she can call upon a specialist. For example, a neurologist might perform certain tests if there is a possibility of brain disorder.

If medical consultations are ordered for your relative, you should not be alarmed. This is not evidence that your relative has some rare and serious disease. Medically-based disorders often are much more easily treatable than disorders that are wholly behavioral. Actually, you could feel reassured by the fact that your relative's psychiatrist has ordered medical consultations, for this suggests that the psychiatrist is carefully looking into all of the possible causes of your relative's problem.

Another reason for scheduling a physical examination of a psychiatric patient is to assess the advisability of prescribing certain psychiatric medications. Some medications cannot be taken safely by people with certain physical conditions. Before prescribing one of these medications, the psychiatrist will want to make sure that it is safe.

PSYCHOLOGICAL TESTING AND OTHER EVALUATIONS

Sometimes, a psychiatrist may feel that it is advisable to develop additional information about the patient through psychological tests or other evaluations. Some of these tests may seem mysterious, but they are not hard to understand once you know what they are about, and they can provide a great deal of useful information.

Probably the best-known psychological test is the so-called I.Q. test, which measures intelligence. A person is given multiple-choice or other questions, and answers are tallied to produce a score that is regarded as indicative of a certain level of mental development.

Adult psychiatric patients usually are not given I.Q. tests unless there is some question about whether mental retardation is a factor in the patient's disturbance. However, children or adolescents are often given such tests, since psychiatric problems in childhood and adolescence often are linked to abnormally high or low intellectual development.

Other well-known psychological tests include the so-called projective tests, in which subjects are asked to interpret pictures, designs, patterns, or other visual materials. The tests are called "projective" because the visual stimuli themselves are neutral—they do not mean anything—and the subject supplies, or "projects," interpretations that can reveal the subject's own thoughts and feelings.

In one of the best-known projective tests, the Rorschach Inkblot Test, subjects look at a series of inkblots and tell the examiner what images or emotions each of the inkblots evokes. The value of the test does not lie in the character of the inkblots or their ability to provoke certain types of responses. Rather, Hermann Rorschach, the Swiss psychiatrist who developed the test, observed over a number of years that certain groups of people responded to the same inkblots in the same ways. More specifically, psychiatric patients who had been diagnosed as schizophrenic responded in much the same way as each other but dramatically differently from the ways in which other psychiatric patients responded.

Once the patterns of responses were established, the inkblot test became a diagnostic tool. In other words, a subject's responses could be used to suggest a tentative diagnosis or to help confirm a diagnosis that was based on other evidence.

A test that operates on the same principle is the Thematic Apperception Test, or TAT, in which subjects are shown pictures and asked to make up a story about what is depicted. One picture shows two women, one obviously older than the other. Both have rather gloomy facial expressions. Some subjects might create a story in which the two are a mother and daughter who have just had a quarrel. Other subjects may regard the women as sisters grieving over the death of a parent. Obviously, the stories that subjects create are fed by the subject's own experiences and feelings and can be extremely revealing about the subject's frame of mind.

Still other psychological tests involve drawing pictures or giving reactions to pictures or words. For example, in "word association" tests, the examiner provides one word and the subject replies with the first other word that comes to mind.

Yet other psychological tests can help identify brain damage by calling on the subjects to exercise verbal or other skills, such as copying line drawings, which are controlled by certain portions of the brain. Another type of test is made up of questionnaires about the subject's ideas and preferences. The best known of these, the Minnesota Multiphasic Personality Inventory (MMPI), seeks responses to hundreds of items. The responses are, as with responses to the Rorschach, TAT, and other projective tests, compared to those of many other people whose personality characteristics are known.

A patient may at first feel uneasy or resentful about these tests. Some patients may fear that the examiner can use the test to peer deeply into the patient's mind and extract all sorts of long-concealed secrets. Others will simply regard them as a waste of time, or even feel that the tests are biased against them. However, the tests have proved their value over a great many years. Used judiciously, they can very quickly supply a lot of information that can assist the psychiatrist in diagnosing the patient's problem.

Along with psychological tests, psychiatrists may order evaluations by social workers, educators, or other professionals. A social worker might interview family, friends, or acquaintances about the patient's behavior or the family's living conditions. If the patient is a child or adolescent, a teacher might assess performance in school, especially if the patient seems to have a learning disability.

Once all of the evaluations have been made, it will be up to the psychiatrist to put them together and develop a diagnosis—in effect, a theory about exactly what the patient's problem is.

Through all of this, you—the patient's relative—may have a great deal of contact with the psychiatrist or you may have little or none. How much contact you have will depend to an extent on the nature of the patient's condition, the working style of the psychiatrist, and the treatment approach of the hospital.

The more disabled the patient is, and the less able or willing to provide information, the more important it is for the psychiatrist to get information from you or other sources. By extension, if the patient can give a fairly detailed and reliable personal history, the psychiatrist may prefer not to speak to anyone else about the case. Thus, you may feel left out, or not as involved or well-informed about your relative as you would like to be.

Sometimes the psychiatrist will not discuss your relative with you or others because of concerns about confidentiality. The patient should feel that he or she has a private relationship with the psychiatrist and can "open up" about problems—even if these problems involve matters about which the patient does not want anyone else to know. Although you may resent what you regard as the psychiatrist's "keeping secrets" from you, you probably will acknowledge on reflection that all of us—yourself included—have certain secrets, certain private bits of information or thoughts or experiences that we do not want revealed to anyone else. If the patient is to work well with the psychiatrist, the patient must feel that the psychiatrist will not violate the relationship's confidentiality, even to members of the patient's family.

This is not to say that the confidentiality of the relationship is absolute, as in the Roman Catholic Church's "seal of confession." If I concluded that my patient intended to kill someone, I would feel obliged to warn the person whose life was in jeopardy. Also, courts may under certain circumstances require psychiatrists to reveal information about certain dealings with a patient. And insurance companies, with signed permission from patients, demand certain information as a way of ensuring that the patient is not being given any treatment beyond what is authorized by the policy.

In general, psychiatrists will be very careful about revealing anything that a patient might not want revealed. Thus, while you can expect periodic progress reports from your relative's psychiatrist, and while you may also receive advice about how to deal with the patient and how to assist in his or her recovery, you cannot expect the psychiatrist to disclose your relative's secrets to you.

The confidentiality of the patient-psychiatrist relationship is a cornerstone of the "therapeutic alliance"—that is, the cooperative effort between patient and psychiatrist to work together on the patient's problems. I'll put special emphasis on that word, "work." Psychiatric treatment should not be a passive experience for the patient. The patient should work actively and as hard as possible to overcome his or her problems. Normally this will not happen unless the patient feels that the psychiatrist is working for him or her and not in someone else's interest.

Thus, the psychiatrist may believe it necessary to establish strict limits about what he or she says to the patient's relatives or friends. At the same time, the psychiatrist usually will be interested in obtaining as much pertinent information as possible about the patient. You and other people who know the patient can contribute importantly to the psychiatrist's objectivity as he or she works with the patient.

One of the most effective means of involving relatives in a case without violating the patient's trust is to schedule meetings at which the psychiatrist, the patient, and one or more relatives are present. In this setting, everyone can exchange information, yet no one is talking behind someone else's back.

A meeting like this can be useful to the psychiatrist in another way; he or she can see how you and the patient get along with each other and how you divide roles and responsibilities. Granted, you probably will hesitate to be completely open about your concerns in front of the patient, and the patient may hesitate to be completely open in front of you. Also, the presence of the psychiatrist probably will inhibit both you and the patient from relating to each other exactly as you would if no one else were present. All the same, such meetings can provide valuable diagnostic data for the psychiatrist and can also help improve your relationship with the patient, something that will be very valuable after the patient has been discharged from the hospital.

5

Psychiatric Diagnosis

Attempts to describe mental disorders go back to ancient times, but most of the early descriptions are extremely vague. "Hysteria," for example, deriving from the Greek word for womb, was applied to a variety of symptoms that the ancient Greeks believed were caused by movements of the uterus. Precise categories of emotional disorder are a development of the last hundred years, and the categories that are generally employed today are much more precise than those of even two or three decades ago.

You may wonder why categories are necessary. After all, most of us can recognize if someone is having significant emotional problems. We need only observe changes in behavior and listen to what the person says he or she is experiencing. However, for treatment to be effective, it is important to know more about a case than the fact that a person is "having emotional problems." Only by identifying the unique aspects of each category of problem can we communicate about them and develop treatments for the entire category. If we did not group emotional disturbances, we would be starting virtually from scratch with every new case.

The description of mental disorders historically has been approached from various perspectives. One system of classification measures degrees of impairment. Another categorizes "families" of symptoms. Still another relates behavior to the ideal as postulated in one or another theoretical framework. None of these approaches has won universal acceptance, and there is still considerable disagreement today about the best way to classify mental disorders. However, hospital psychiatrists and many other mental health workers, recognizing the need for a common language, have adopted an official list of diagnoses developed by the American Psychiatric Association. These can be found in the *Diagnostic and Statistical Manual of Mental Disorders, Third Edition*, or DSM-III.

No one claims that this classification is perfect; psychiatrists may not always agree about distinctions among the categories—or even about whether certain behaviors belong in a catalogue of "disorders." However, DSM-III seems to be the best approach devised thus far, and most psychiatrists with whom you have contact will speak in terms of its diagnostic categories. I have used these categories throughout this book, just as I do in my everyday work.

DSM-III lists more than two hundred distinct categories, each regarded as significantly different from all of the others. In this chapter, I'll discuss and provide case examples of the disorders that are seen most often in hospitals. However, if you have been told that your relative has a specific disorder, please do not assume that his or her case will be identical to the one presented here. There are considerable and significant differences among cases within a category, and each case has its own unique features. Therefore, use this chapter's case examples as an overview and a source of general knowledge, but do not regard them as all-embracing. If you are interested in learning more about a specific diagnosis, discuss it with your relative's psychiatrist or read more about it in a general text or a book specifically about that diagnosis.

The categories of mental disorders are listed here in more or less the same order in which they appear in DSM-III, and the descriptions within quotation marks are drawn from DSM-III.

MENTAL RETARDATION

The term "mental retardation" refers to "significantly subaverage intellectual functioning" with an I.Q. (Intelligence Quotient) of 70 or below and concurrent deficits or impairments in adaptive behavior.

Subcategories of retardation relate to I.Q. scores, with a score of 100 considered "normal." Retardation is considered "mild" if the patient has an I.Q. score between 50 and 70, "moderate" between 35 and 49, "severe" between 20 and 34, and "profound" below 20.

Mental retardation is not often the primary diagnosis in an acute care psychiatric hospital. This is because the disorder generally is recognized in the early years of life, and treatment is begun then.

If retardation is mild or moderate, outpatient treatment usually will be enough. Functioning at a higher level of intellectual performance generally is possible, and training programs are available at special schools or community service agencies. If retardation is severe or profound, inpatient care may be necessary, but this care generally will be provided at a special institution for retarded patients or at a county or state hospital. Such care usually is chiefly custodial. There is little if anything that can be done to substantially improve the mental performance of such patients. Treatment therefore focuses on helping the patients function as comfortably as they can within their limitations.

When retarded persons are hospitalized at an acute care facility, retardation generally is a secondary diagnosis. In other words, the patient has a psychiatric problem other than retardation. The problem may be but is not necessarily exacerbated by retardation.

A case history:

A 28-year-old mentally retarded women had been getting along rather well living at home and attending a special workshop for retarded people four times a week. However, when her father died suddenly of a heart attack, she was unable to understand and to adjust to losing him.

Within a few days she grew increasingly frightened and desperate, and she started to believe that people were following her and trying to break into her house. She felt increasingly out of control and soon became a serious problem for her mother. The young woman would scream and shout at the mother, and on several occasions she actually struck the mother. Worried about her own safety, the mother arranged hospitalization.

Upon admission, the patient became even more agitated. However, she improved rapidly with small doses of antipsychotic medication, which stopped her fears and feelings of persecution. She also underwent crisis intervention therapy, and the psychotherapist's supportive treatment helped her grieve for her father and deal with the loss of him.

> The woman's psychiatrist developed a plan of treatment that stressed occupational therapy (treatment through performance of work-related tasks) and other activities with which she was familiar from the special workshop. She also participated in and benefitted from group therapy (psychotherapy in which several patients are treated at the same time).
>
> Within a week, the woman was sufficiently calm and comfortable enough to be discharged. Living once again with her mother, she was able to suspend medication. However, she continued in outpatient therapy for several months to learn to deal more effectively with mourning. Her mother joined her for some of these outpatient sessions and was able to get some help for her own problems dealing with her husband's death.

Mental retardation is often present with other psychiatric diagnoses. People who are mentally retarded may, because of their limited intellectual capacity, have a more difficult time coping with stress than other people do, and may be more susceptible to other psychiatric problems.

If your relative is mentally retarded, your support and encouragement will be especially important during inpatient therapy, for mentally retarded people are especially susceptible to fear, confusion, and disorientation. Your encouragement and reassurance while the patient is away from his or her usual environment can help speed a favorable response to treatment.

ATTENTION DEFICIT DISORDER WITH HYPERACTIVITY

This condition, which occurs in childhood and adolescence, is known also as "hyperactive child syndrome," "hyperkinetic syndrome," "minimal brain damage," and "minor cerebral dysfunction." Three features characterize it: inattention, impulsivity, and hyperactivity.

Because of *inattention*, the child often fails to finish things that he or she starts, often seems not to listen, is easily distracted, has difficulty concentrating on schoolwork or other tasks requiring sustained attention, and has difficulty remaining interested in a play activity.

Because of *impulsivity*, the child often acts before thinking, shifts excessively from one activity to another, has difficulty organizing work, needs lots of supervision, frequently interrupts conversations and classroom instruction, and has difficulty waiting his or her turn in games or other group situations.

Because of *hyperactivity*, the child runs about or climbs on things excessively, fidgets excessively and/or has difficulty staying seated, moves about inordinately during sleep, and acts as if "driven by a motor."

The condition is usually treated on an outpatient basis but occasionally requires hospitalization.

A 12-year-old boy was living in a residential treatment center that specialized in children with emotional problems. His inattention, easy distractability, and poor concentration on schoolwork or play were regarded as manageable. Even his constant fidgeting and apparent need to be "on the go" were well within the range of behaviors with which the treatment center dealt regularly.

After a time, however, the boy's impulsivity and low frustration tolerance began to get out out hand. He would have temper outbursts and would pick fights with other children, whom the staff could not always protect.

Admitted to an acute care psychiatric hospital, he was evaluated by a psychiatrist, a psychologist, a neurologist, and a schoolteacher. His perceptual and motor skills were tested, and his interaction with other children was observed. He also was given a complete physical examination.

Based on the neurological and other medical consultations, among other inputs, the psychiatrist changed the medication the boy had been taking. The boy also spent some time in psychotherapy, art therapy, and other programs at the hospital. He participated enthusiastically and conscientiously because he wanted to do well and return to his friends at the residential treatment center.

Within a few weeks, all testing and treatment were complete and the boy became less hostile. He was discharged to the residential treatment center, where he was much better able to work on developing social and academic skills.

CONDUCT DISORDER

Children and adolescents in this category show a "repetitive and persistent pattern of conduct in which either the basic rights of others or major age-appropriate societal norms or rules are violated." The children are classified as "socialized" or "unsocialized" based on the presence or absence of adequate social bonds. They are classified "aggressive" or "nonaggressive" based on the presence or absence of a pattern of aggressive antisocial behavior.

Typical behavioral problems include persistent truancy, substance abuse, repeated running away from home overnight, persistent serious lying, stealing, vandalism, rape, breaking and entering, fire-setting, mugging, assault, thefts, extortion, purse-snatching, and armed robbery.

Youngsters with conduct disorders often are treated as outpatients within their communities or at juvenile detention centers. However, such a youngster may also be sent to an acute care psychiatric hospital for evaluation.

> A 14-year-old boy was brought to a special adolescent treatment unit by his parents. For years he had been truant from school frequently, had smoked cigarettes and consumed alcoholic beverages, and had used marijuana and other "street drugs" whenever he could obtain them. He had run away from home several times, and he had been caught stealing.
>
> He had been incarcerated at a detention center for juveniles several times on charges of burglary or possession of drugs. Released on probation, he assaulted a schoolmate and was suspected of assaulting several others. His probation officer recommended psychiatric hospitalization.
>
> The psychiatrist's diagnosis of conduct disorder was confirmed by the boy's behavior at the hospital. He lied incessantly to members of the staff, brought in illegal drugs, and frequently got into fistfights with other teenagers.
>
> When the psychiatrist instituted a so-called behavior modification treatment plan (the boy could earn extra privileges by behaving better), the boy's behavior improved. However, even after a hospital stay of several weeks, he still violated the hospital's rules whenever the rigid structure of his individualized treatment program was relaxed.
>
> After consulting with the boy's parents and his probation officer, the psychiatrist arranged transfer to a live-in facility that specialized in troublesome adolescents. Neither the boy nor his parents wanted out-of-home placement, but they preferred it to the alternative—a state prison for juveniles—partly because there he would have a better chance to learn to deal with his problems.

ANOREXIA NERVOSA

This eating disorder, which is especially prevalent among teenage girls, is characterized by intense fear of becoming obese, disturbance of body image (for example, claiming to "feel fat" even when emaciated), severe weight loss, and refusal to maintain even a minimal normal body weight.

Anorexia nervosa can lead to death by starvation. Because it is so often fatal, it may require inpatient hospital treatment.

A case in point:

A 17-year-old girl began to worry her parents when her weight declined dramatically. They noticed that she began handling her food strangely. Sometimes she would rearrange small pieces on her plate or hide food and secretly throw it away.

As she continued to lose weight, her parents grew increasingly concerned and began monitoring her more closely. They discovered that sometimes she indulged in eating binges, and then made herself vomit. She also seemed to be abusing laxatives.

Her parents arranged for outpatient treatment with a psychotherapist. The girl insisted that there was nothing wrong with her. She said that she was dieting because she was fat. In fact, she was perilously underweight and so malnourished that even her menstrual periods had stopped. The psychotherapist diagnosed her as anorexic but could not succeed in getting her to eat. The psychotherapist recommended hospitalization.

In the hospital, the girl was assigned to a treatment program based on behavior modification principles. Initially, she was required to stay isolated in bed without visitors. She was told that she would be given privileges to have physical and social activities on a graduated basis as she began to gain weight.

She resisted treatment and tried to convince her parents to take her home. However, they realized that she was running the risk of death by starvation or from a complication of her physically weakened condition. Because of their rights and responsibilities as parents, they required her to remain in the hospital.

When she saw that she was not going to get what she wanted by her approach, she began to eat. Soon she had gained a little weight and was participating more willingly in psychotherapy. She began to understand that she was not overweight and that, to an extent, she had been using the false claim of being overweight as part of her problems in relating to boys.

Soon she was eating regularly and had obtained through the behavior modification program the full range of hospital privileges. She now participated in psychotherapy and showed excellent progress. She was discharged to outpatient followup.

OTHER DISORDERS FIRST EVIDENT IN INFANCY, CHILDHOOD, OR ADOLESCENCE

There is a variety of other disorders that are first evident during infancy, childhood, and adolescence. Some have physical manifestations, such as tics, stuttering, bed-wetting, fecal incontinence, or sleepwalking. Others involve unreasonable anxiety (for example, an excessive fear of being separated from one's parents). Still others, termed "developmental disorders," involve inability to perform intellectually or emotionally at the same level as is usual at a given age.

Certain developmental disorders are rather narrow in focus, dealing with one skill or subskill: for example, a child may have difficulty saying certain sounds, or may transpose letters or words while reading. Other developmental disorders are broader in focus: the child, while competent in reading, will have trouble with arithmetic, or vice-versa. More generally, the pervasive developmental disorders such as infantile autism involve impaired social relationships, markedly abnormal speech, and resistance to change.

These disorders, except for the more severe progressive developmental disorders, usually are treatable on an outpatient basis, and it is rare to find any of them as a primary diagnosis in an acute care psychiatric hospital. However, one or more of these disorders are often seen in youngsters who have been hospitalized for other reasons.

ORGANIC MENTAL DISORDERS

The essential feature of these disorders is a "psychological or behavioral abnormality associated with transient or permanent dysfunction of the brain." In other words, the patient acts abnormally because of some physical damage to the brain.

PRIMARY DEGENERATIVE DEMENTIA

The term "dementia" has been applied to a wide assortment of conditions over the years and at one time was used synonymously with "madness" and "insanity." Today, psychiatrists apply it exclusively to organic loss of specific intellectual abilities. In other words, intellectual function is impaired, usually permanently, as a result of some influence upon the brain.

The signs and symptoms of dementia include memory impairment, impairment of abstract thinking (for example, difficulty in defining words and concepts), impaired judgment, aphasia (a disorder of language due to brain dysfunction), agnosia (failure to recognize or identify objects despite intact sensory function), and personality change.

One of the best known of these disorders is senile dementia, more fully described in DSM-III as "primary degenerative dementia, senile onset." It is an insidious onset of dementia without any other specific cause and with a uniformly progressive deteriorating course.

The symptoms in such cases may be mild enough that the person can be cared for at home without much difficulty. However, once the symptoms become severe, management at home will become difficult and hospitalization may be warranted.

A 73-year-old woman had lived alone for quite some time and had managed very well. Gradually, however, she began to have trouble remembering things—not only dates and people's names and matters of that sort but also appointments and important tasks. On several occasions, she forgot to turn off the water or the stove before leaving her apartment. Once she flooded the bathroom, and on another occasion she almost started a fire.

Recognizing that she could no longer live safely on her own, she moved in with her daughter. Unfortunately, her condition continued to deteriorate. She would have periods of confusion. Sometimes she could not identify familiar objects, such as a fork or a shoe. She became inattentive to personal appearance and hygiene, and she withdrew from contact with old friends.

After perhaps a year of living with her daughter, she began to have delusions of persecution. Forgetting where she had put something, she would accuse her daughter of stealing it. Eventually she became convinced that her daughter wanted to get rid of her, perhaps even kill her. She began to lock the door of her room, and she slept with a knife under her pillow.

When the daughter found her mother walking around the apartment brandishing the knife, the daughter decided that psychiatric evaluation was warranted. At an acute care hospital, the mother was given medical tests to rule out the possibility that her symptoms might be caused by some treatable disease. When the tests proved negative, the diagnosis of "primary degenerative dementia, senile onset," was made.

The woman was given small doses of antipsychotic medications and was kept under observation for several days. She very quickly stopped being suspicious of her daughter. She also became much calmer than she had been on admission, when her state was quite agitated.

Her basic dementia was not treatable. Thus, she would spend the rest of her life forgetting things and experiencing confusion. However, with the medications, the suspicions and delusions that had accompanied this state were eliminated. The woman was able to return home and live comfortably with her daughter.

Sometimes the symptoms of degenerative dementia start at age 65 or earlier, in which situation the diagnosis is "presenile" rather than "senile" dementia.

A 56-year-old executive was regarded by colleagues and employees as extremely intelligent, competent, and dynamic. He enjoyed an excellent family life; he had been happily married for thirty years and was the proud father of two successful young adults.

Suddenly and inexplicably, he began to have problems with memory. Then, just as quickly, he began making serious errors of judgment, several of which were very costly to his company. Alarmed, he sought treatment as an outpatient, but no explanation of his behavior could be found.

Fearful of damaging the company's best interests if he remained at work, he took a sabbatical leave. At home, his disorientation and general confusion quickly worsened. His physical condition also deteriorated; his movements slowed, and he took on a shuffling gait.

He was taken to an acute care psychiatric hospital for evaluation. Medical tests were performed. No treatable causes were found to explain the dementia.

In cases of this sort, the disease usually proceeds inexorably, with the patient continuing to deteriorate, sometimes at an increasingly rapid rate. Death occurs within a few years.

The executive returned to his home, where his wife cared for him for as long as she could. He continued to deteriorate rapidly. When he spoke, he was incoherent. Usually, he could not even remember his own name. He could not feed himself, and he became incontinent (unable to control urination and defecation).

He was admitted to a nursing home, where he died after several months.

Note: dementia is quite different from delirium, which is an entirely different condition. Unlike dementia, delirium is characterized by a clouding of consciousness, perceptual disturbances (such as misinterpretations, illusions, or hallucinations), incoherent speech, insomnia or daytime drowsiness, increased or decreased psychomotor activity, disorientation, and/or memory impairment. These clinical features tend to fluctuate over the course of a day.

SUBSTANCE-INDUCED ORGANIC MENTAL DISORDERS

The word "substance" is used in psychiatry to indicate any physical agent that can affect the brain: alcohol, psychiatric medications (for example, tranquilizers or antidepressants), the so-called "street drugs" (such as marijuana or cocaine), caffeine or tobacco. Organic mental disorders have been connected with all of these substances, usually relating to intoxication or withdrawal.

Substance-induced disorders often result in hospitalization. The signs and symptoms of alcohol intoxication are familiar: with recent ingestion of alcohol, maladaptive behavioral effects (for example, fighting, impaired judgment, or interference with social or occupational functioning); physiological signs (slurred speech, incoordination, unsteady gait, flushed face); and psychological signs (mood change, irritability, talkativeness, impaired attention).

ALCOHOL WITHDRAWAL

Usually, simple intoxication does not lead to hospitalization, but serious psychiatric and other medical problems can occur during withdrawal. This occurs after cessation or reduction of heavy and prolonged ingestion of alcohol. Unlike intoxication, it is caused by the body's adjustment to the absence of the abused substance. Signs and symptoms include tremor of the hands, nausea, vomiting, sweating, weakness, rapid heartbeat, change in blood pressure, anxiety, depressed mood, and irritability. A case:

> *A 42-year-old man voluntarily entered an alcohol treatment program. He had been on a three-month binge, drinking a daily ration of a quart of liquor and a six-pack of beer.*
>
> *In addition to psychological treatment for alcoholism, he needed medical treatment for withdrawal. Withdrawal may lead to delirium tremens, the "D.T.'s," characterized by tremors, nausea, general weakness, rapid heartbeat, profuse sweating, hallucinations, seizures, and, in some cases, even death. When medications are used, the intensity of most of these signs and symptoms can be reduced.*
>
> *Within a week, the man felt well physically and was discharged to outpatient psychotherapy. It took longer for his mind to "clear" so that his thinking seemed as sharp as before.*

It is not unusual for chronic alcoholics to develop *dementia* to some degree. The condition is characterized by poor memory, confused thinking, frequent errors in judgment, and generally inept performance of other intellectual tasks. Obviously, the ability to work and to socialize also becomes impaired, and the accompanying problems can create additional emotional difficulties.

Other substances also cause intoxication, withdrawal-related reactions, and other mental disorders that can lead to hospitalization. For example, the problems attending withdrawal from barbiturates or similarly-acting drugs are very much like the problems attending withdrawal from alcohol.

> *A 23-year-old woman was admitted for treatment of dependency on barbiturates. She arrived at the hospital "loaded" with drugs she had taken that day.*
>
> *To have suspended medications entirely for her would have created severe withdrawal signs and symptoms—shakiness, nausea, vomiting, general weakness, rapid heartbeat, changes in blood pressure, anxiety, irritability, depression, or even delirium. Thus, the psychiatrist set up a schedule to lower her medication gradually over a number of days before stopping it altogether.*
>
> *The schedule was observed, and the woman accomplished withdrawal without inordinate discomfort.*

OPIOID WITHDRAWAL

Opioid withdrawal occurs after prolonged, heavy use of an opioid (heroin, morphine, and other opium-based or opium-like agents) or after administration of a narcotic antagonist following a briefer period of use. Symptoms may include secretion of tears, runny nose, dilated pupils, sweating, diarrhea, yawning, increased blood pressure, rapid heartbeat, fever, and insomnia.

Years ago, addicts frequently were forced to withdraw abruptly—to go "cold turkey." Currently, methadone, a synthetic narcotic, is often used to ease the pain of withdrawal.

Of course, once withdrawal has been accomplished, the problem of overcoming dependency on the drug still remains, and that is a psychological problem that will require continued treatment on an inpatient or outpatient basis or at a recovery home. (In DSM-III, "substance-use disorders" are classified separately from "substance-induced organic mental disorders;" I will discuss them and their treatment later.)

Some substance-induced organic mental disorders bear strong resemblance to other psychotic states. For example, amphetamine delusional disorder is in many ways quite similar to paranoid schizophrenia, a condition I will describe later in this chapter.

AMPHETAMINE DELUSIONAL DISORDER and AMPHETAMINE WITHDRAWAL

Amphetamine delusional disorder is a dangerous substance-induced organic mental disorder. It is caused by use of amphetamine or a similarly acting drug over a long period and in moderate or high doses. It is characterized by persecutory delusions and at least three of the following: ideas of reference, aggressiveness and hostility, anxiety, and agitation.

Amphetamine withdrawal is characterized by depressed mood, fatigue, and disturbed sleep. The following case demonstrated both conditions:

> *A 27-year-old man took amphetamines regularly and grew increasingly anxious, irritable, and suspicious. He came to believe that everyone around him—friends as well as strangers—was part of a police network designed to catch him using drugs and possibly*

kill him. His friends knew he needed help and found him locked in his house, refusing to answer the doorbell or telephone. With firm insistence, they were able to persuade him to visit the hospital.

Once there, he became extremely frightened and agitated, threatening people and attempting to attack a nurse. He was calmed somewhat by injections of antipsychotic medications, but, as time passed, he became extremely irritable and depressed.

Over the next several days, he slept a great deal. When he was awake, he repeatedly spoke of wanting to commit suicide. He had to be observed carefully until, about a week later, withdrawal was complete and he was well enough to be discharged to outpatient therapy.

PHENCYCLIDINE (PCP) INTOXICATION

Phencyclidine is a "street drug" known by many names, including PCP, "angel dust," "crystal," "peace pill," "hog," "horse tranks," "super weed," "peace weed," "rocket fuel," and "super grass." It can cause dangerous states while the user is intoxicated as well as mental problems after continued use.

PCP produces such signs and symptoms as increased blood pressure and heart rate, numbness or diminished responsiveness to pain, uncoordinated speech and body movements, euphoria, agitation, anxiety, changing moods, grandiosity, a sensation of slowed time, belligerence, impulsiveness, unpredictability, impaired judgment, and assaultiveness. Symptoms of PCP intoxication may include hallucinations, paranoid ideation, and bizarre or violent behavior.

A case:

A 19-year-old man was brought to a psychiatric hospital by police because he had been screaming irrationally and attacking people with a baseball bat at a shopping center. He had been extremely violent, and it took five police officers to place him in restraints. Friends said he had been using PCP.

At the hospital, he was placed under observation. His intoxication gradually cleared, but he was unable to remember what had happened.

He was kept under observation for three days, then was discharged to outpatient treatment. Even though he did not take any more PCP, he had trouble concentrating and remembering things for several weeks.

HALLUCINOGEN DELUSIONAL DISORDER

LSD and a variety of other hallucinogens—so named because they may provoke hallucinations—can also bring about mental states that require inpatient treatment. Sometimes hallucinations may recur many days or weeks after an initial episode.

> *A 24-year-old woman had taken LSD on several occasions. She believed that the hallucinogenic experience from taking LSD was a way of "expanding her consciousness." On one occasion, she suffered a brief period of intense anxiety and fear (the well-known "bad trip") but friends were able to "talk her down" from it, and there were no apparent side effects or aftereffects.*
>
> *Then she took LSD again, and this time the "trip" was very bad. She was so frightened, suspicious, and agitated that her friends could not calm her. She began running around the room and trying to jump out the window.*
>
> *Her friends, despite being under the influence of the drug themselves, had enough presence of mind to restrain her and take her to a psychiatric emergency room. Her condition was not immediately relieved by psychiatric medications, so she was admitted to the hospital for further observation.*
>
> *Over a period of several days she gradually "cleared" and said she felt like her "old self." However, she suffered several "flashbacks" in which hallucinations returned, accompanied by the fear, suspicion, and agitation.*
>
> *The psychiatrist, believing that she had emotional problems that were made worse by the LSD, recommended on discharge that she begin outpatient therapy. She did. On several occasions during the course of therapy, she had yet other recurrences of the original hallucinations—even though she swore she had not used LSD or any other drug since the "bad trip."*

ORGANIC BRAIN SYNDROMES

Like the age-related dementias and substance-induced states, the organic brain syndromes involve psychiatric problems related to brain malfunction. Sometimes the problem can be traced to injury or disease of the brain, while in other cases the cause cannot be found. Symptoms may include those found in dementia, delirium, amnesia, hallucinations, and depression, as well as such personality changes as explosive temper outbursts, sudden crying, poor social judgment, sexual indiscretion, shoplifting, apathy, indifference, suspiciousness, and paranoia.

A case in point:

> A 26-year-old man began suffering frequent headaches and dizziness. Then he started having trouble remembering things and understanding what was going on around him.
>
> At first he tried to ignore the symptoms, telling himself that they probably were not important and would go away on their own. Soon, however, he became delusional and was persuaded by his parents to seek help.
>
> He was admitted to a psychiatric hospital, where a medical evaluation revealed a brain tumor. The tumor was removed surgically, and the man's mental state improved gradually but never returned completely to normal.

SUBSTANCE USE DISORDERS

Earlier in this chapter I wrote of substance-induced organic mental disorders—that is, conditions resulting from the effect on the brain of alcohol, drugs, or other "substances." The problem in that category of cases was usually either intoxication or withdrawal, although many people incur permanent brain damage as a result of repeated use of certain of these agents.

Another psychiatric problem that relates to such agents—a problem affecting a much larger number of people—is dependency, which need not cause clinically measurable damage to the brain in order to wreak havoc on the lives of substance-users.

Several cases in point:

> • A 47-year-old alcoholic decided to get help when his boss said his job was on the line and his wife threatened to leave him.
>
> • A 32-year-old man who had been running his own business found himself broke and miserable after spending all his money free-basing cocaine.
>
> • A 26-year-old woman had been working as a prostitute to support her addiction to heroin; she sought psychiatric help because she could not bear the thought of continuing to degrade herself because of her dependency on the drug.
>
> • A 36-year-old housewife sought help after deciding that she

could not care for her children and continue using a combination of alcohol, sleeping pills, and tranquilizers.

• *A 21-year-old man sought help after being jailed for an accident he caused when driving while intoxicated; over the previous several years, he had kept himself stoned virtually continuously with marijuana, LSD, amphetamines, and PCP.*

All five of these people were unable to deal with their problems as outpatients and entered a special treatment program for alcohol and drug abusers. The program, conducted at a psychiatric hospital, employed a broad assortment of therapeutic approaches.

The patients confronted each other about their problems in daily group meetings. Because the problems were often similar, the patients were able to offer each other insights, suggestions, and support.

Much of the program was based on the mutual-help approach of Alcoholics Anonymous (AA), which calls upon members to acknowledge that they have a disease and to help each other deal with it. The patients attended meetings of Alcoholics Anonymous and a similar organization, Narcotics Anonymous, both at the hospital and in the community.

They also had regular individual sessions with psychotherapists and substance abuse counselors. They attended lectures, films, and discussions about alcohol and drug abuse, along with meetings of separate groups for male and female abusers.

In some meetings, the patients defined what their goals would be at the hospital. They also made plans for when they left the hospital; they worked out schedules for treatment as outpatients and other schedules for their leisure time which would no longer include drugs.

They learned about themselves by means of such activities as creative writing, aerobics, body-awareness training, and relaxation training. They worked with biofeedback machines to gain control over their bodies' responses to stress.

Family members attended meetings at the hospital and at local organizations such as Al-Anon, an AA-related group for relatives of alcoholic persons. There they learned about the patient's problems, how to deal with them, and how to avoid supporting the patient's alcohol or other drug habits.

When the patients finished with the in-hospital program, they continued in an aftercare program which included regular meetings of Alcoholics Anonymous and Narcotics Anonymous, *family groups, and an "alumni" group that helped the patients keep sober and "straight" outside the protective, structured environment of the hospital.*

Living in a hospital or other structured environment makes it easier for a patient to stop substance abuse. After withdrawal, patients can learn—in the company of their peers—that they are able to cope with life without alcohol or drugs.

SCHIZOPHRENIA

One of the most common diagnoses in psychiatric hospitals is schizophrenia, a severe condition characterized by bizarre, grandiose, religious, and persecutory delusions; auditory hallucinations; incoherence; markedly illogical thinking; and deterioration from a previous level of functioning in such areas as work, social relations (isolation and withdrawal), and self-care.

A case example:

A 29-year-old man with a diagnosis of paranoid schizophrenia was hospitalized for the fourth time because he had again become very confused and paranoid. He had dropped out of school after his first decompensation and had not been able to work since. He was receiving disability payments and lived isolated in a rooming house with no friends.

Six months before being admitted for the fourth time, he had stopped taking his antipsychotic medication, and his usual symptoms gradually returned. He had delusions that people were following him, were out to get him, could read his thoughts, and could control him. He felt that he understood great truths that other people could not, and he also felt that he was a uniquely special human being—although he was no longer convinced that he was Jesus Christ, as he had once believed.

He heard voices of people telling him that they were his friends, commenting on his actions, calling him names, telling him to do things (such as to put objects in certain places), and even suggesting dangerous actions (such as attacking people). The hallucinations had become increasingly loud and persistent, and at times he would cover his ears or shout to try to drown them out. His thinking and speech became quite confused.

In the hospital he resumed taking his medication, and within two weeks he showed improvement. The voices spoke to him less frequently and seemed to come from farther and farther away, finally fading away completely. He became less frightened and was able to relate to others more easily and normally.

He began to eat properly and to keep himself and his clothing clean. When he was discharged, he was urged to continue taking his medicine and get outpatient therapy to help maintain the good level of functioning that he had achieved.

SCHIZOPHRENIFORM DISORDER

This condition displays the symptoms of schizophrenia during a brief period of time (by definition, between two weeks and six months), and often is the first manifestation of a chronic schizophrenic disorder. In most cases, hospital treatment is advisable.

A 21-year-old man underwent rapid mental deterioration over a period of several months. He came to believe that he played a central role in a colossal struggle over world control and domination. He felt that he was in jeopardy of being destroyed by the people around him and that the future of the entire world depended on his surviving their attempts to overpower him. When his family suggested that he seek psychiatric help, he disagreed vehemently and locked himself in his room.

When he refused to come out of the room voluntarily, his family arranged for him to be taken forcibly to a hospital. He at first resisted treatment, denying that he had any problems. Given medication, he showed rapid improvement. He was discharged to outpatient treatment, but he never went to the scheduled follow-up visits. Several months later he decompensated and had to be rehospitalized.

BRIEF REACTIVE PSYCHOSIS

In this disorder, psychotic symptoms appear immediately after a recognizable psychosocial stressor that would evoke significant symptoms of distress in almost anyone—for example, death of a loved one or loss of one's home in a fire. The clinical picture may include emotional turmoil, delusions, hallucinations, and disorganized behavior.

A case:

A 15-year-old girl came home from school one day to find the body of her mother, who had been killed by a burglar. The girl was, understandably, extremely upset; however, instead of giving vent to her emotions by screaming or crying, she became withdrawn and refused to express her grief. After a few days, she became physically uncoordinated and began speaking in phrases that did not make sense.

Hospitalized, she quickly began to return to normal. After several days, she was discharged to outpatient therapy. Not surprisingly, she remained grief-stricken for months, for she had been emotionally close to her mother and now had to deal with not only the psychological impact of her mother's loss but the inescapable memory of having found the body. However, she continued in psychotherapy and did not again show the extreme disorganization that she had exhibited initially.

AFFECTIVE DISORDERS

Another category of psychiatric conditions is the affective disorders, in which the patient's view of the world usually does not differ substantially from that of the rest of us but the patient's mood is disturbed.

The most widespread symptom of the affective disorders—and the most common mood disturbance in all of psychiatry—is depression. Some people experience it as a reaction to events (loss of a loved one, collapse of well-laid plans, et cetera), but these so-called "reactive" or "exogenous" cases of depression represent only part of the total. In a great many other instances, depression cannot be related to events in a person's life (and is therefore termed "endogenous").

DEPRESSION

Depression is a major feature of several mental disorders. The clinical picture includes depressed mood (feelings of being sad, blue, hopeless, low, down in the dumps, irritable), feelings of inadequacy, and decreased effectiveness or productivity at school, work, or home. Other elements of the clinical picture include decreased attention or ability to think clearly, social withdrawal, a pessimistic attitude, tearfulness or crying, loss of interest or pleasure in usual activities and pastimes (including sex), poor appetite and weight loss (or sometimes, increased appetite and weight gain), trouble sleeping (or, again, inordinately large amounts of sleep), agitation, a feeling of being "slowed down," loss of energy, fatigue, thoughts of suicide or the wish that one were dead, and feelings of worthlessness, self-reproach, and guilt.

The diagnosis of depression takes into account such factors as the severity of the signs and symptoms of depression, other symptoms which may accompany the disturbance of mood, and whether or not there is a recurring pattern.

In some cases, the person has had experiences that might realistically provoke a depressive reaction but seems to suffer a level of depression disproportionate to the intensity or duration of the experiences.

A case in point:

A 63-year-old woman had evidenced mild levels of depression for almost twenty years; during this time her children grew up and left home, she experienced menopause, and she retired from work. Her feelings of sadness and gloom intensified after her husband died and she was left living alone.

She said she felt unhappy constantly and had little hope for the future. She lost her appetite and began to lose weight. She had trouble sleeping, and woke early every morning, which was the worst time of day for her.

She became restless and agitated, and she tended to pace and to talk in a pressured manner. She lost interest in things that previously had held her attention, and she constantly felt tired. She also began to worry and feel guilt about minor things that she might have done wrong—for example, failing to greet the postman cheerily when he delivered the mail.

The depression continued for three years and eventually became more severe than what she had felt during the first few months after her husband died. She began to think that she had nothing to live for and would be better off dead. Her daughter suggested that she enter a hospital, and, although the mother thought that hospitalization would not help, she consented to be admitted.

Treated with antidepressant medications, she began to show improvement within two weeks. By the end of three weeks she was well enough that she could go home and continue her medication and therapy on an outpatient basis.

BIPOLAR DISORDER, MANIC EPISODE

In bipolar disorder, periods of depression alternate with one or more distinct episodes of mania. In the manic episode, the person experiences a predominantly elevated, expansive, or irritable mood, including such manifestations as an increase in activity, physical restlessness, being more talkative than usual, racing thoughts, inflated self-esteem, grandiosity, a decreased need for sleep, distractibility, buying sprees, sexual indiscretions, foolish business investments, and reckless driving.

> *A 36-year-old man, involved romantically with a woman for two years, believed that he was in love for the first time in his life. He was making plans for their wedding when she suddenly broke off the relationship, saying that she was in love with someone else.*
>
> *Instead of becoming depressed, he entered a bizarre manic state. He continued to talk about his former girlfriend as if they still were together; he told many people of their supposed upcoming marriage, as if the wedding had not been cancelled.*
>
> *He seemed to have developed an inordinate amount of energy. He was always "on the go," sometimes appearing agitated and irritable as he hurried through his busy schedule, but more often appearing happy and upbeat. He was especially energetic at work, yet slept only a few hours each night. He began speaking in an intense, pressured way, and his attention seemed to race pell-mell from one topic to the next.*
>
> *Soon he began going to bars and nightclubs, where he would spend large amounts of money on women he had just met. This sort of behavior was highly uncharacteristic of him, but when friends suggested that he was acting in an unusual way, he told them that they merely were envious that he was having such a good time.*
>
> *He next invested in a questionable business venture with someone he had met in a bar. He borrowed the money for the investment, and he soon borrowed more money, much of which he gave away to people he had just met. Soon he was delinquent on many loans and was a candidate for bankruptcy.*
>
> *His parents urged him to see a psychiatrist, but he insisted that nothing was wrong with him. Finally his parents arranged for him to be hospitalized against his will. Treatment included antipsychotic medication and lithium, and within a few days he had calmed considerably and began speaking less and less unrealistically.*

The antipsychotic medication was discontinued and in less than three weeks he was discharged on lithium to outpatient followup. In the course of his psychotherapy he showed appropriate depression as he dealt with the loss of his girlfriend. He understood that with his diagnosis it was important for him and his family to watch for a recurrence of symptoms.

ADJUSTMENT DISORDERS

By definition, an adjustment disorder is "a maladaptive reaction to an identifiable psychosocial stressor," with "impairment in social or occupational functioning or symptoms that are in excess of a normal and expected reaction to the stressor." The assumption is that the disturbance will eventually remit after the stressor ceases or, if the stressor persists, when a new level of adaptation is achieved.

Hospitalization may be necessary during the period of adjustment. Usually treatment focuses on the adjustment, and hospitalization is not lengthy.

A 36-year-old woman admitted herself to a psychiatric hospital because she felt she was suffering a "nervous breakdown." She normally was able to handle many things very well but had suffered a series of reversals that became too much for her to handle.

Her husband, whom she had tried to help with his drug abuse, left her with four children to care for along with holding a full-time job. Her purse was snatched as she was walking down the street, and she was knocked down and suffered broken ribs and a broken arm in the assault. Then she was involved in a minor automobile accident, and this cost her some money as well as loss of time from work.

These stresses left her progressively less able to cope. Burdened with worries, she often did not feel like eating, and she suffered from lack of sleep. Her general health began to deteriorate, and she became depressed, having frequent crying spells and a pervasive sense of hopelessness.

In the hospital she was able to achieve some respite from her problems, and she also obtained practical aid, especially from social services, in dealing with some of these problems. Individual psychotherapy helped her organize her thinking, and group therapy provided support from other patients who sympathized with her problems. The patients acknowledged that they themselves

would not be able to cope with such a series of misfortunes, either.
Within a week, she was able to leave the hospital. Gradually
she put her life in order again.

PERSONALITY DISORDERS

Personality disorders are deeply ingrained maladaptive patterns
which cause distress or impairment in a person's functioning. There
are several different types:

PARANOID PERSONALITY: A person with a paranoid personality is suspicious and mistrustful of others. Afraid of being tricked or
harmed, he or she often is cautious and guarded, questions the
loyalty of others, and is overly concerned about hidden motives and
special meanings. He or she is hypersensitive, and is quick to take
offense.

SCHIZOID PERSONALITY: A person with this disorder appears
cold and aloof. He or she has close friendships with no more than one
or two persons, and does not show warm, tender feelings for others.
Detachment from the environment and daydreaming are common,
as well as difficulty expressing aggressiveness or hostility.

SCHIZOTYPAL PERSONALITY: Characteristics include odd
speech, superstitiousness, feeling strange or unreal, and belief in
"magical thinking" (for example, being convinced that thinking
something might cause that thing to happen).

HISTRIONIC PERSONALITY: A person with a histrionic, or
"hysterical," personality shows overly dramatic attention-seeking
behavior and irrational tantrums. Interpersonal relationships lack
genuineness, even if superficially warm and charming. A person
with this disorder is characteristically egocentric, inconsiderate of
others, demanding, and prone to manipulative suicidal threats.

NARCISSISTIC PERSONALITY: This personality has a grandiose sense of self-importance or uniqueness, and fantasies of unlimited
success, power, brilliance, beauty, or ideal love. Interpersonal relationships show a constant need for attention and admiration, lack of
empathy, and an expectation of special favors from others.

ANTISOCIAL PERSONALITY: A person with an antisocial
personality does not accept social norms with respect to lawful
behavior and responsibilities such as work, parenting, maintaining
enduring attachments, and honoring financial obligations. Lying,
repeated drunkenness or substance abuse, thefts, and physical fights
are characteristic.

BORDERLINE PERSONALITY: This personality shows unstable and intense interpersonal relationships, marked mood shifts, frequent displays of temper, potentially self-damaging impulsiveness and unpredictability, uncertainty about identity, and chronic feelings of emptiness or boredom.

AVOIDANT PERSONALITY: Features of the avoidant personality include hypersensitivity to rejection, unwillingness to enter into relationships unless given unusually strong guarantees of uncritical acceptance, social withdrawal, desire for affection and acceptance, and low self-esteem.

DEPENDENT PERSONALITY: A person with a dependent personality passively allows others to assume responsibility for major areas of life because of inability to function independently, and subordinates his or her own needs to those of persons upon whom he or she depends in order to avoid any possibility of self-reliance and independence.

COMPULSIVE PERSONALITY: This personality is unduly conventional, serious and formal, and such a person shows stinginess, perfectionism, and insistence that others submit to his or her way of doing things. There is excessive devotion to work and productivity, and preoccupation with rules, procedures, and trivial details.

PASSIVE-AGGRESSIVE PERSONALITY: Someone with a passive-aggressive personality may express resistance to demands for adequate performance indirectly through procrastination, dawdling, stubbornness, intentional inefficiency, and "forgetfulness."

Although the treatment of personality disorders alone is usually possible on an outpatient basis, hospitalized patients often have personality disorders in addition to their other problems.

For example, borderline personalities are common among the psychologically disabled. A patient with a diagnosis of schizophrenia may also have a paranoid, schizoid, or schizotypal personality. And drug abusers often have an antisocial personality.

Personality disorders often affect treatment of the "primary" diagnosis, that is, the main reason a patient is admitted. For example, passive-aggressive behavior can hinder inpatient treatment just as it interferes with effective functioning outside a hospital.

OTHER CATEGORIES

The diagnoses discussed above are not the only things that may be considered in evaluation. Three other approaches, or ways of looking at the overall picture (called "axes" in DSM-III), might also be considered.

The first of these categories describes physical disorders from which a person suffers and which may be relevant to treatment of the psychiatric disorder. For example, a 32-year-old man with cerebral palsy became depressed following the breakup of a long romantic relationship. His neurological condition was recognized as having an important influence on his emotional problem.

A second category involves considering how much or how little stress is enough to lead to the loss of normal functioning. For example, a 34-year-old man had an obsessive-compulsive disorder; he was afraid that something would happen if he did not carefully perform many series of acts in exact order each day. One of these was locking the door of his house; he had to return several times to check that it was locked before he finally went to his planned destination. When he lost his job as a result of arriving late too many times, the stress was more than he could handle in combination with his obsessive-compulsive condition, and hospitalization was necessary. Decompensating in response to only mild stress suggests that a person cannot handle pressure very well, particularly when compared to a healthier person suffering more severe stress.

The third category for evaluating people entails noting the highest level of functioning they showed during the preceding year. For example, a 24-year-old man never held a job for more than a few months, while a 43-year-old woman was successfully raising three children while working part-time. Other things being equal, greater strength and higher level of functioning usually mean better prospects.

These categories add to the diagnosis information that can be very helpful in understanding the person, helping with therapy, and anticipating the future.

6

Treatment In
Psychiatric Hospitals

The mission of an acute care psychiatric hospital is to help patients recover as quickly as possible from the problems that brought them there so that they can be discharged and get further treatment as outpatients, if necessary.

As I have pointed out in earlier chapters, inpatient treatment is appropriate only when outpatient treatment is not enough—that is, when a patient is dangerous or disabled or has to be watched while medication or other treatment is being started or adjusted. However, in some respects, a hospital is not a desirable environment. The patient must conform to a set routine, whether he or she wants to or not; being in the company of many other patients may be unsettling; and hospital care is very expensive. Obviously, therefore, the ideal situation is one in which the patient stays in the hospital for no longer than is absolutely necessary.

THE TREATMENT PLAN

After the psychiatrist has made an initial assessment of the patient and his or her problem, it is necessary to decide how to approach treatment. The treatment plan will be devised by the psychiatrist, the nursing staff, and specialists from such programs as occupational therapy, biofeedback, and special activities. Their collaboration will be accomplished in conferences and in communications through notes on the patient's chart.

The treatment plan will take into account the diagnosis, the expected length of stay in the hospital, and what the general course of treatment is expected to be. Goals will be noted and special problems listed, including matters such as difficulties with development, family, environment, social contacts, and legal problems. Certain handicaps, such as deafness, may need special attention.

After the problems have been listed, judgments will be made about how to deal with them. The treatment plan must explain how goals are measured and when they are expected to be reached. There must be some assessment of when the patient has accomplished what can best be done in the hospital and should be discharged to outpatient services. Periodic review during hospitalization will check how well the goals are being met. The treatment plan will be modified based on the patient's response to problems and on recognition of new problems.

The patient and others involved in the case will take part in treatment planning. Planning provides a rational framework to guide efforts to benefit the patient's well-being.

THE TREATMENT TEAM

The task of accomplishing the patient's treatment as quickly and effectively as possible does not fall on just one person but on an entire team of highly-trained specialists.

PSYCHIATRIST—The psychiatrist has primary responsibility for the management of the case. He or she may obtain consultations, as needed, from a wide variety of other specialists.

INTERNIST OR OTHER MEDICAL SPECIALIST—Specialists in internal medicine or other medical fields ranging from neurology to gynecology may be called upon to perform evaluations of the patient's physical state.

PSYCHOLOGIST—Psychological tests are administered by psychologists, who may also be called upon to perform psychotherapy (as may other members of the treatment team).

NURSING STAFF—A nursing supervisor is in charge of all nursing activities at the hospital. In addition, there is a head nurse in charge of each ward and another nurse in charge of each ward for every shift. The ward staff usually includes not only nurses with R.N. licenses but also people with such titles as orderly, psychiatric technician (P.T.), mental health aide (M.H.A.), and nursing assistant or nurse's aide (N.A.). Therapists with other degrees such as a master's degree in social work (M.S.W.) or credentials in marriage, family, and child counseling (M.F.C.C.) may also be on the staff. A clerk does secretarial work, such as copying a doctor's orders onto medication cards for use in dispensing drugs, preparing material to be sent with a patient upon transfer to another institution, et cetera.

OTHER HOSPITAL PERSONNEL—People in various departments carry out yet other functions within the hospital. For example, activities such as occupational therapy, art therapy, dance therapy, and recreational therapy generally are provided by a separate staff that specializes in these activities.

The social service department usually arranges disposition and placement to other institutions. The department staff also make arrangements for financial assistance and work with the patient's family on various matters. In fact, at some hospitals the family spends more time with the social service staff than with the psychiatrist, who gives attention exclusively or almost exclusively to the patient.

If school-age children are hospitalized, a teacher provides the instruction that they would otherwise miss by being out of school.

The hospital's dietician, in addition to preparing a nutritious menu for all patients, develops special menus for patients who have dietary deficiencies, medical problems, or other reasons for not being able to observe the normal menu.

Some hospitals have entire divisions—separate from other units—that specialize in programs for alcoholics, drug abusers, teenagers, geriatric patients, or patients requiring only part-time hospitalization.

In virtually every hospital there is a laboratory for medical tests and a pharmacy to prepare medications. There usually is a library that the staff uses for reference and a unit where confidential medical records are stored carefully so that they are readily available for future use by authorized staff.

There is also an administrative unit, made up of an administrator and staff, a business office, an admissions office, and a billing department. Other necessary services are provided by housekeeping and maintenance departments and a telephone switchboard.

Hospitals also have committees that establish guidelines for treatment procedures and other activities. The doctor in charge may be called the chairman, medical director, or chief of service. Other doctors work under his or her direction. In addition, committees monitor such areas as utilization of the hospital's services, standards of medical practice, doctors' credentials, medical records, prevention of spread of infectious diseases, continuing education, bylaws and rules of the medical staff, special procedures (such as electroconvulsive therapy), and safety procedures.

SCHOOLS OF THERAPY

There are many different schools of thought about human psychology, and there are many approaches to treatment of emotional disorders. A large number of these schools and approaches focus primarily on thoughts and feelings. You may be familiar with the names of the founders of some of the better-known schools and approaches, such as Sigmund Freud, Carl Jung, Alfred Adler, Karen Horney, Harry Stack Sullivan, Wilhelm Reich, and Erik Erikson.

These scientists all founded "psychodynamic" schools— schools in which there is an attempt to understand what goes on in the mind in terms of various forces, structures, and theoretical concepts. The central idea is that by understanding ourselves we can have greater control over our behavior and our mental life.

The original theories often referred to defense mechanisms, a concept that still is important today. The early idea was that people feel anxiety and put up defenses in order to cope with it. In Chapter Two, in discussing resistance to treatment I dealt with such defense mechanisms as denial and projection. You may hear these terms used by people who are treating your relative, as well as in everyday conversation.

Another concept from the psychodynamic theories is that part of what goes on in the mind is "unconscious"—that is, we are not consciously aware of it, even though it affects thinking and behavior. That the unconscious exists can be demonstrated in various ways. For example, dreams make more sense when we assume they are produced by mental stimuli of which we are usually not aware. Since the unconscious affects the way we think, feel, and act, efforts are made to understand more about it.

You probably are familiar with the idea, also originating in psychodynamic theory, of stages of development, such as the oral, the anal, and the phallic stages. According to this theory, a person must learn to deal with specific issues at each stage, and problems may linger if they are not mastered when they should be. For example, a person fixated on oral feeding may inappropriately demand emotional "feeding" from others as an adult.

Another approach to psychotherapy is behaviorism, which places emphasis on observable behavior rather than on thoughts and feelings. The central idea of behaviorism is that people learn to behave in certain ways as a result of the rewards and punishments they receive when they behave in these ways. For example, in a benchmark behaviorist experiment, Russian physiologist Ivan Pavlov arranged for a bell to be rung every time certain dogs were fed. After a while, the dogs began salivating whenever they heard the bell, even though no food was present.

The learning of such a response is termed "conditioning," and someone who has learned the response is described as having been "conditioned." In one technique of behaviorism, "operant conditioning," a person learns to behave in a certain way by being rewarded for behaving that way—and perhaps also by being punished for behaving in any other way.

Following is an example of operant conditioning in hospital psychiatry:

A teenager may be behaving in a way that has gotten him or her into trouble. The psychiatrist and other members of the hospital staff will make it clear to the teenager that there must be a change in behavior if the teenager is to earn such privileges as going on outings or being transferred to a more desirable ward. Every time the teenager behaves in the desired way, he or she is given the "reward" of the desired privilege (or the preliminary "reward" of one or more points toward a total necessary for a desired privilege). If the teenager misbehaves, the privilege may be withheld, or points may be withheld or subtracted.

Behavior therapy has proved very effective with geriatric patients, who often are not oriented toward examining their inner feelings but who may react positively to getting rewards for doing such things as talking to each other or becoming involved in activities instead of withdrawing to their rooms.

The field of sociology can also provide insights that are useful in psychiatric treatment. For example, a patient may lack experience in getting along with people because initial social relationships were faulty or because of psychological handicaps that interfere with successful relationships. Learning to get along in social situations can help patients function better after they have been discharged. Socialization and avoidance of too much isolation can help patients maintain the gains they achieved during therapy in the hospital.

Yet another approach to psychiatric treatment is biological and usually involves medications. Biochemical reactions underlie physiological changes that go on inside the body. These include changes that affect the brain, which, in turn, governs behavior. Messages that travel along nerves within the body and inside the brain are transmitted by electrical impulses, and these impulses depend on chemical reactions. These reactions may meet interference from abnormal blood composition, hormones, or many physical diseases. This interference may, in turn, affect thinking or behavior.

Obviously, genetically-caused disorders are biochemically determined. However, a biological approach may be useful even if one assumes that past experience is responsible for a person's current behavior, since the changes that the environment has (in theory, anyway) brought about must be programmed inside the person on a physical basis. Medication can often cause changes within the body and bring about normal functioning. For example, if a person hears voices when no one is around, the voices may be made to "go away" if an appropriate medication is employed. Whatever the original reason that the person heard these voices, the merits of the biological approach are proved empirically. Medications have become so important in hospital psychiatry today that I have devoted the next two chapters of this book to them.

In thinking about the differences among the various schools of thought, you may wonder how anyone can decide which approach, if any, is correct. Your puzzlement probably will increase if you read opposing academic arguments by classicists of one school or another. However, do not let any of this entice you to attach yourself philosophically to one school or another. The fact is, in modern hospital practice, a combination of approaches usually is used.

For example, a depressed patient may be treated with psychodynamic insight-oriented psychotherapy to understand the causes of the depression. Behavior therapy might also be used to discourage withdrawal and self-pity and also to encourage active participation in such activities as occupational therapy and body movement. Socialization with other patients can reduce isolation. And antidepressant medications often will bring dramatic relief.

INDIVIDUAL, GROUP, AND MILIEU THERAPY

Psychotherapy may be performed in a variety of settings. The oldest and most widely studied setting is "individual psychotherapy," which means simply that the psychotherapist and the patient relate to each other one-to-one rather than in a group.

If the psychotherapist's approach is psychodynamic, the focus will be on the interaction of conflicting forces within the patient. If the approach is behaviorist, the approach will be on training the patient to behave in certain ways, using rewards and perhaps punishments.

On an outpatient basis, individual psychotherapy may be chiefly exploratory—an unhurried, detailed examination by psychotherapist and patient of what the patient's inner feelings and conflicts may be. In a hospital, the approach is generally more supportive than exploratory; that is, the emphasis is not on a deep understanding of all the underlying influences on a problem but rather on dealing with the problem as quickly and as effectively as possible. This is because the usual emphasis of treatment in an acute care psychiatric hospital is more on helping a person pull together quickly than on taking apart and examining different elements of the person's mental make-up. The long process of "depth" psychotherapy is left for an outpatient setting.

Many inpatient programs involve "group psychotherapy," which allows patients to discuss problems in an organized way, make efficient use of a skilled therapist's time and energies, and provide feedback from peers about various problems. The group may consist of all the patients on a particular ward or unit or of patients who fall into a particular category, such as adolescents, alcoholics, or drug-abusers. In some hospitals, families might be invited to join groups of patients, or a special group session might be arranged for one patient and his or her family, friends, and other significant people.

"Milieu therapy" refers to the concept that a patient's surroundings in a psychiatric hospital may contribute to the patient's improvement. Dr. Maxwell Jones and other therapists developed the idea that the psychiatric ward is a "therapeutic community" that the patient enters after being unable to manage successfully in the larger "community" of the outside world. Acting in his or her usual way, the patient repeats the same kinds of relationship problems as in the outside world. In the therapeutic community, however, these actions do not pass without comment but are looked at and discussed so that the patient can better understand his or her behavior.

The hospital's staff also plays roles in the therapeutic community, and the behavior of members of the staff can be examined along with the behavior of patients. There often will be discussion of the ways patients feel about the behavior of the staff—and of the ways members of the staff feel about the behavior of patients. The feedback that the patient receives can help him or her learn to behave in ways that lead to more harmonious relationships. Thus, milieu therapy helps the patient get along better in the larger community after discharge from the hospital.

ACTIVITY THERAPY
AND SPECIAL PROGRAMS

Therapy involving various activities allows patients to learn about themselves, develop skills, and discover how to get along better with other people.

Activities might include art, music, dance, body movement, creative writing, or preparing a journal. Life-skills such as cooking or grooming may be taught. Other parts of the program might include leisure counseling and relaxation techniques, occupational therapy, and such hobbies as sewing, ceramics, or gardening. Recreation might include bingo, bowling, volleyball, dances, movies, or outings to local parks.

In these activities, patients develop social skills and learn about their own reactions and abilities. They have to solve the problems of how to participate and organize their reactions. In the process, they cultivate recreational and leisure interests to pursue after being discharged.

Here are some examples of how activities are used therapeutically:

• Treatment for a lethargic, depressed patient might include activities designed to lessen withdrawal and stimulate both mental and physical performance. Calisthenics, dance, outings from the hospital, or even repetitive menial tasks (such as cleaning) might be effective.

• Activities that encourage limit-setting might be helpful for a patient who is manic (i.e., already overly active and excited). For instance, the patient might be confined to his or her room and assigned activities that call for minimal bodily movement.

• A schizophrenic might benefit from expressing bizarre ideas and violent fantasies in drawings or paintings. Giving vent to such ideas artistically can help the patient become aware of what is bottled up inside—and, in the process, relieve pressure from internal forces that the patient has been struggling to keep under control.

• A delinquent teenager or destructive child might be encouraged to discover creative potentials, which, if positively directed, can modify behavior and help raise the person's self-esteem. For example, a boy who continually gets into fights might be encouraged to construct things with hammer and nails.

Special programs may be part of a patient's treatment plan. For example, an adolescent might attend sex-education classes or be given training in peer and family relationships. An alcohol and drug program may provide information about drugs and nutrition; participants might also meet with former patients who can talk about their own experiences staying sober, and preparations can be made for aftercare, which might include membership in Alcoholics Anonymous or other self-help groups.

Biofeedback sometimes is used as a therapeutic tool. Machines measure such physiological activities as muscle tension, perspiration, skin temperature, pulse, brain waves, and rate of breathing. Patients can look at a meter or listen to a tone that signals immediately what is going on inside the body. Patients can then train themselves to relax under pressure and to gain some measure of control over physiological responses. In the process, patients also gain awareness of how thoughts and feelings affect the body.

Videotape is another modern medium that can help a person gain self-awareness. A patient can behave spontaneously in front of the camera and afterward study with some detachment what his or her behavior is like.

Not every hospital will have all of the programs that I have described. Each hospital has its own group of activities, and treatment plans are designed to emphasize the most relevant activities for each patient.

PROBLEMS FAMILIES FACE DURING A RELATIVE'S TREATMENT

A wide variety of problems may arise during your relative's treatment. In the paragraphs ahead, I offer case examples of several typical ones. If such problems (or others) arise, talk with your relative's psychiatrist or other members of the hospital's staff. They can help you understand what is happening, and they also can give you specific advice about how you can help.

In one of the most commonly encountered problems, the patient manipulates the family against the psychiatrist and the hospital in an effort to avoid treatment.

> A 14-year-old girl was brought to the hospital by her mother because she was no longer manageable at home.
>
> For years the girl had been unwilling to abide by the house rules her mother established. She was truant from school and on several occasions ran away from home. She abused drugs, including marijuana, barbiturates, and occasionally other substances.
>
> The mother and father were legally separated. The mother refused to let the daughter live with the father, and a trial of living with grandparents did not work out; the grandparents' initial tolerance was exhausted quickly by the daughter's disobedience to even their far-more-relaxed rules.
>
> The patient was angry about being admitted to a psychiatric hospital. As soon as the mother left, the girl tried to run away, provoking a struggle with the staff. The struggle ended with the girl being restrained to a bed by leather straps.
>
> Within fifteen minutes, she grew calm and agreed that if she was released from the leather restraints she would not again attempt to run away. When nurses removed the restraints, the girl immediately telephoned her mother, saying the staff had beaten her severely and that she could show bruises on her wrists (where she had fought against the restraints) to prove it.

The mother spoke to the psychiatrist and the nursing staff, who explained what had happened. The mother refused the daughter's request to be taken home. The daughter then telephoned her father, saying that the mother and the psychiatrist said it would be all right for the father to take the girl home. When the father sought to verify this with the mother and the psychiatrist, he was told the truth. The father also refused to take the girl home, but, in the process of discussing the situation with the mother, he got into another of the many bitter quarrels that had punctuated their marriage. The phone call ended with the two at loggerheads.

The daughter now turned again to the mother, repeating the approach she had employed with her father, saying that the psychiatrist and the father had agreed that the girl should be discharged. When the mother was not persuaded, the girl turned again to the father.

She made a series of calls to both parents, trying to make them feel guilty for putting her in the hospital. She insisted that they could not possibly love her if they would not take her home. And she said that if they did not obtain her release now, she would hate them and never talk to them for the rest of her life.

In the hospital, she refused to take part in the program of therapy that was scheduled for her and threatened to run away again. She telephoned a girlfriend and asked her to bring in some marijuana, hoping that using drugs would result in her being discharged for breaking the hospital's rules. She also intended to let her parents know about the marijuana; she believed she could make them worry about forcing her into an institution where drug abuse was rampant.

She emphasized her sexual attractiveness with makeup and carefully chosen clothing, and she acted seductively toward male patients, provoking jealous quarrels among them. She tried to elicit pity and sympathy wherever she could. She also tried to divide the loyalties of the members of the treatment team, then provoke combat between her "allies" on the team and her "adversaries."

When she was disciplined for breaking rules, she claimed that she was being punished unfairly. She tried to embarrass members of the staff who refused to grant her privileges that she had not earned and who did not allow her delinquent behavior to go unchallenged.

Another technique that she used to foster quarrels among people around her was to distort statements that she carefully extracted from people. For example, she would get her psychiatrist to agree that something must have been wrong in her background at home or she would not have her present problems. She then *would telephone her mother and report that the psychiatrist had made derogatory remarks about the way she had been raised.*

In trying to turn her mother against the psychiatrist, she would make up stories. For example, she told her mother that she was getting a pass one weekend. The mother cancelled an important engagement to be free at that time. When the mother arrived to pick up the daughter, she learned that the girl and the psychiatrist had never discussed a pass. The girl then tried to persuade her mother that the psychiatrist had promised a pass but later cancelled it and that he therefore was the person responsible for inconveniencing the mother.

This patient, using manipulative techniques that she had learned in a pathological family situation, was able to create a fairly constant uproar around her because it took a certain amount of time for the people involved in her manipulations to talk to each other and determine what everyone had actually said about a given matter. The girl usually was not fully conscious of what she was doing, and the psychiatrist's attempts to get her to recognize her manipulations usually led to evasive denial.

The girl's behavior represented a true psychological problem in that she was only partly aware of her actions and only dimly conscious of her motivations. The goal of therapy was to have her stop using these manipulations and, instead, develop a mature personality with better ways of relating to others. The girl was acting out her problems with her manipulations, and if these manipulations were allowed to succeed (for example, if she convinced her parents to take her out of the hospital), the goal of therapy would be defeated.

Manipulations by patients to avoid treatment can have serious results, as in the following case:

A 28-year-old woman had been depressed for some time about problems with the man that she wanted to marry. When he broke up with her and started dating one of her friends, she started thinking about killing herself.

When her mother found her crying in her room, the daughter spoke of suicidal wishes. The mother was concerned and convinced the daughter to go to the emergency room of a nearby psychiatric hospital. A psychiatrist recommended hospitalization, but the daughter argued strongly against this and convinced the mother to take her home.

> *During the night the mother heard moaning from the daughter's room. When she investigated, she found that she could not wake the daughter from a dazed, lethargic state. There was an empty pill bottle on the nightstand. The daughter was taken back to the hospital and had to undergo a tracheotomy (cutting into the windpipe and inserting a tube) for restoration of breathing.*

In some cases, there are bitter struggles between patient and family:

> *A 26-year-old woman had been hospitalized four times. She was uncooperative about getting outpatient treatment between hospitalizations, and she usually gave away her money to panhandlers on the streets, where she spent most of her time. As a result, she had to eat at charity dining rooms and live in hotels of even lower quality than she ordinarily would have been able to afford from her disability checks.*
>
> *When she finally became so confused that she could no longer manage on her own, she would return to her parents' house and quarrel with them for several days about going to the hospital. The exasperated parents finally would convince her to seek admission, and she would do so docilely. However, once she was inside the hospital and her parents came to visit, she would have violent quarrels with them. In these loud and repetitious exchanges, the parents would try to convince her to cooperate with treatment and she would loudly refuse, complaining about the staff, the treatment program, and the side effects of her medications.*
>
> *During each visit, the daughter would angrily tell her parents to go away and never come back. Then, as soon as they got home, she would telephone them and beg them not to leave her at the hospital all alone. She would implore them to get her out of the hospital or, at the very least, to keep her company while she was there.*
>
> *By the time she was discharged, she always made a big point of saying that she did not want to depend on her parents ever again. However, she always returned to their home—and, eventually, to the hospital.*

The conflict between dependence and independence can cause genuine torment for parents who want to see their child happy and do not want to abandon him or her. Alas, patients can play on those feelings and approach parents in such a way that the parents can hardly refuse a request.

If you find yourself in such a situation, you may feel torn by the desire to help your child and the knowledge that he or she will later probably turn against you again and say things that will hurt. It may be helpful for you to discuss this with a psychotherapist and try to work out a way of responding to the manipulations of your child.

Sometimes patients resist efforts to get them into treatment because they enjoy some aspects of being psychotic:

> *A 31-year-old man, diagnosed as chronic schizophrenic, had a reputation as a real "character." His outrageous style of dress made him stand out on the street. He was in outpatient psychotherapy with several psychiatrists simultaneously and got as many pills from each of them as he could. He then sold the pills or traded them for cocaine or other "street drugs."*
>
> *The man drew attention to himself by claiming that he was an important (though eccentric) person from a distant place. He was able to present his make-believe personality in a way that was sufficiently attractive and entertaining that people tolerated and even enjoyed him.*
>
> *He liked to use amphetamines and to act as outrageously as he could. He was far less happy when his behavior was more reasonable and controlled.*

Sometimes people enjoy having hallucinations and use drugs to increase them. Some people may feel more comfortable playing a role than facing the fact that their behavior is not considered normal; they find it easier to establish the kind of relationships they prefer by using manipulative or noticeably deviant behavior.

For example, a husband may be able to get attention from his wife by acting in such a way that she perceives him as needing her help and stops what she is doing to come to his rescue. Sometimes people feel happier with the notion that they cannot be helped and must live a marginal lifestyle than dealing with the fact that family members no longer want anything to do with them because of their unreasonable behavior.

Occasionally a person enters a psychotic state for only a limited time because of temporary stress. In these cases, intervention may not be necessary. (However, please do not assume that any case with which you are involved will be like the following.)

> *A 25-year-old woman had suffered repeated decompensations spaced several years apart. During each decompensation, she*

became severely depressed and delusional. However, she realized which of her symptoms were not reality, and she was able to pass through these phases by retreating to her apartment and cutting off contact with the rest of the world for a few days. By reducing stress, she could pull herself together and resume her regular functioning.

Sometimes the objection to treatment comes from relatives rather than from the patient.

A 17-year-old girl was hospitalized with hallucinations and delusions. Her father, who had been hospitalized several times with schizophrenia, died from complications of alcoholism some years earlier. Her mother was quite difficult to get along with and maintained an intrusive, controlling influence over the girl.

Although it was clear that the girl needed treatment in a residential facility, the mother objected adamantly. The mother particularly opposed the use of antipsychotic medication, saying that she once had tried her husband's medication and had suffered stiff muscles. She was convinced that her daughter would suffer the same side effect.

The mother harrassed people at the hospital and at the agency trying to arrange placement for long-term care at another institution. Neighbors had provided documentation that the child had been beaten severely at home, but the mother insisted that everything was fine and that the girl should come home instead of being referred to another institution. She insisted that she knew what was best and that treatment was not what her daughter needed.

A parent's struggle to control a psychotic child can reflect the parent's own problems. When a child suffers from psychiatric problems, cooperative support by parents of early treatment can have lifelong benefits. Parents may guiltily feel that the child's problems are their fault and may want to deny that any problem exists (so that they do not feel that they have passed on a genetic disposition to a mental disorder or that they have treated their child badly). Guilt, denial, and interference with treatment can be difficult matters to deal with, but the best interests of the child should be kept foremost in mind.

Sometimes friends sabotage treatment, as in the following case:

A 29-year-old woman, diagnosed as alcoholic, also used many other drugs, including narcotics and stimulants. She paid for her drugs and for those of her addicted boyfriend by being a prostitute.

This woman's dependency was not restricted to substances: she was desperately attached to her boyfriend, even though he repeatedly beat her, stole her money, and spent time with other women. She convinced herself that he loved her, even though all her friends thought he was using her.

When he stole an especially large amount of money and left her, she entered the hospital for detoxification and therapy. However, two weeks later, her boyfriend ran out of money and wanted her to return to prostitution for him.

Even though her craving for drugs had decreased, she was unwilling to face the difficult emotional problem of resisting his demands, changing her lifestyle, and becoming independent. He convinced her to sign out of the hospital against medical advice.

If you have any feeling that therapeutic work with your relative is in jeopardy, discuss your concerns with your relative's psychiatrist.

7

Psychiatric Medications:
General Considerations

If your relative is hospitalized for psychiatric treatment, the likelihood is that he or she will be given medications. You may have misgivings about this. Psychiatric medication has received a lot of bad press.

There is a widespread public image of patients shuffling about a dismal, bare-walled ward in dazed and semistuporous states, barely knowing who they are. This image has been fostered by many movies, plays, books, and newspaper articles, as well as by stories told by hospital visitors and by patients themselves.

The charge has been levied that medications are used for the convenience of the staff, in order to avoid bedlam. (The word "bedlam," interestingly enough, comes from a mispronunciation of "Bethlehem," a psychiatric hospital in London where many years ago visitors would pay a small admission fee to amuse themselves watching the patients.) It has been said that most patients are "saner" than the staff, which uses drugs to turn them into easily-controllable zombies. It also has been said that if patients resist this abuse, they will be punished with additional medication.

Such contentions, generally unwarranted, are regarded by many people as fact. The fact is that medications have made an immeasurable contribution to the well-being of mentally disturbed men and women.

People suffering a brief episode of psychotic disintegration can, with certain drugs, quickly reintegrate themselves (that is, overcome the episode). Meanwhile, many patients who otherwise would have to spend the rest of their lives in a mental hospital can, thanks to psychiatric drugs, be discharged to nursing homes or return to their families.

Psychiatric drugs have brought about a revolution in the treatment of mental disorders. Until these drugs were introduced, the number of hospital beds occupied by psychiatric patients was increasing progressively. Ever since, the number has been declining.

Drugs that are effective against psychoses, which are characterized by a loss of contact with reality, were introduced in the 1950s. The first to come into continued widespread use had the brand name Thorazine and the chemical name chlorpromazine. (A drug's brand name is created by the manufacturer, usually with the goal of easy pronunciation and recollection; the chemical name is a collection of syllables—often difficult to pronounce and remember—representing the drug's ingredients. There are as many brand names for a drug as there are manufacturers; however, all the brands have the same chemical name.)

When researchers were testing Thorazine for use in surgical anesthesia, they noticed an interesting effect. It produced a tranquil state without excessive sedation or drowsiness, and it proved to be an ideal agent for calming exceptionally agitated psychiatric patients. It is the first of a class of modern drugs now known as antipsychotic agents, neuroleptics, or, informally, "major tranquilizers."

Thorazine and similar drugs—quite a few have been developed over the years—have a remarkable effect on psychotic states. Unlike sleeping pills or other agents which cause overall sedation, these drugs can attack specific psychotic symptoms (for example, hallucinations and delusions) without impairing other mental functions, such as alertness.

Shortly after the introduction of the antipsychotics, another class of medications, the antidepressants, came into use. Antidepressant drugs proved capable of alleviating even the most severe depressions and enabled once-suicidal people to resume normal lives. The alternative in many cases would have been long-term hospitalization or death.

These drugs have largely replaced the convulsive therapies, which had been in use since the 1930s. (The convulsive therapies, which will be discussed in detail later in this book, relieve such symptoms as depression.)

About the same time, another class of drug was developed: antianxiety agents, sometimes called minor tranquilizers. They provide relief not only from anxiety but also from insomnia and other problems.

In 1970, lithium was approved for use in this country and provided a specific and effective treatment for mania. Other drugs—including Antabuse (disulfiram), which is used to combat alcoholism—have provided additional evidence that medications can zero in on specific problems with extraordinary effectiveness.

This is not to say that there are no difficulties attending the use of psychiatric medications. Every medical procedure has its risks. Penicillin has saved countless lives but can be fatal to people who are allergic to it. X-rays, which greatly advanced the science of medical diagnosis, must be used judiciously lest they encourage the development of certain cancers. A small fraction of surgical patients who undergo general anesthesia will be killed by the anesthetic procedure itself; the odds are long, but the risk cannot be denied.

Likewise, there are risks in psychiatric medications. As with any other medical procedure, it is necessary to weigh the risks against the potential benefits; although the chances are small that a patient with a ruptured appendix will die from the anesthetic, there is significant likelihood that the patient will die if surgery is not performed. The alternative to using psychiatric drugs may be to remain psychotic, nonfunctional, and—in many cases—institutionalized for years.

The argument has been advanced that drugs relieve symptoms without attacking the cause of the underlying psychiatric disorder. This may be true in some cases but not in others.

If a psychiatric problem is the result of a simple chemical imbalance in the body, a drug (by correcting the imbalance), can sometimes solve the problem—for example, when depression is caused by lack of thyroid hormone. But in most cases, psychiatrists do not yet fully understand the biological causes of paranoia, depression, and other symptoms. And yet, antipsychotic, antidepressant, and other drugs bring about improvement on some biochemical basis. It would, of course, be preferable to discover a way to overcome the causes of a patient's problems; hopefully, medical science will soon do that. In the meantime, the medication permits more or less normal functioning in someone who otherwise would be seriously impaired or dead.

A corollary argument is that patients should learn to deal with their problems through procedures without the use of drugs, such as psychotherapy. I agree that psychotherapy is usually preferable when it can be used effectively. However, in many cases, it simply is not possible to bring about improvement through psychotherapy alone, and in other cases improvement cannot be achieved within a reasonable time, while medications have proved repeatedly to be rapidly effective.

It is desirable in medicine that procedures should be employed which promise the optimum result in the shortest time and with the least risk. If psychotherapy alone is enough, then psychotherapy alone should be employed. If medications hold out the promise of speedier recovery, then medications should be considered.

Once a psychiatrist has determined that medications should be used, there are still many decisions to be made.

Most psychiatric conditions respond to more than one drug. The psychiatrist must take into account the effectiveness of the various agents as well as the agents' side effects, then choose the drug or combination of drugs which is likely to provide the greatest benefit with the least risk.

Another consideration is dosage. It is usually preferable, whether in psychiatry or other branches of medicine, to use as little medication as possible to achieve the desired effect. If there is doubt that the effect can be achieved with a certain dose, a larger dose will be prescribed, assuming, of course, that the side effects are not prohibitive.

Still another consideration is the form in which the medication will be administered. Pills are easier to handle, but liquids might be advisable if there is some doubt that a patient will swallow pills as prescribed. A drug might be injected to achieve faster absorption by the body of the drug's active ingredients or if a severely agitated patient refuses to take the medication by mouth. One antipsychotic is available in an injectable form which is effective for a week or two, and sometimes even longer.

Yet another consideration is the schedule of doses. Most people find it easier to remember taking medication once a day—say at bedtime or on arising—while sometimes physiological factors demand spreading out smaller doses throughout the day.

The situation becomes even more complicated if a patient suffers from more than one symptom—for example, both anxiety and depression. Several drugs may be required to deal with these conditions. In other cases, a single symptom may call for the use of more than one drug. For example, in the acute manic phase of bipolar (or manic-depressive) disorder, a psychiatrist might order lithium for treatment of mania and an antipsychotic agent to bring certain psychotic symptoms under control more quickly.

If more than one drug is being used, the drugs may interact—sometimes magnifying certain effects of each, at other times working against each other, and at still other times combining to produce side effects. This is yet another factor that the psychiatrist must take into account.

The entire field of psychiatric medication is quite young, and new drugs are being developed all the time. As time passes, more and more is being learned about the best ways to use the various drugs.

Prescribing medication is not a purely scientific enterprise but actually something of an art. The judgment and experience of the prescriber are extremely important. Individual psychiatrists have their own "favorite" medications—those with which the psychiatrist has historically achieved the most satisfactory results—and each psychiatrist has his or her own preferred approaches to dosage, mode of administration, scheduling, et cetera.

Obviously, it would be presumptuous to say that my approach is better than that of my colleague. It would be even more presumptuous of me to advise you about how to judge the approach of your relative's psychiatrist. This does not mean, however, that you should not have a role in your relative's use of psychiatric medications. I'll discuss that role later. First, let's look at some reasons why patients resist taking medications.

COMMON OBJECTIONS
TO USING MEDICATIONS

Psychiatric patients often resist taking the drugs that have been prescribed for them.

Sometimes a patient's resistance is easily understandable. For example, someone who is in the manic stage of bipolar (manic-depressive) disorder often finds the experience quite enjoyable. He or she feels cheerful, energetic, capable of functioning effectively with just a few hours' sleep, and in full command of life's vicissitudes. He or she may know at some level that things will change as the manic stage gives way to a period of depression. But this won't happen until some time in the future. Meanwhile, there is all this energy, all this excitement, all this activity. The temptation is strong to enjoy it while one can.

Likewise, alcoholics may prefer to continue drinking rather than taking some drug such as Antabuse, which will make them nauseated when they ingest even small amounts of alcohol. True, their continued use of alcohol may prove seriously injurious physically in addition to prolonging no less serious behavioral problems. But the alcoholic feels an irresistible craving for the mental state which alcohol provides.

In other situations, patients' resistance to medication is less easy to comprehend. For example, a schizophrenic or depressive may refuse treatment even though without it he or she suffers painful experiences.

Sometimes the patient's refusal is an expression of anger and rebellion against a relative, a concerned friend, the psychiatrist, or the whole of society. The patient may resent the demands being made on him or her and expresses that resentment by refusing to accede.

Other patients who refuse to take medications say they fear addiction. In fact, such worry usually is groundless. Most psychiatric medications, such as antipsychotic drugs, antidepressants, and lithium, are not physically addictive; they do not cause a "high" (that is, euphoric feeling), and generally abuse does not occur. The patient might worry about becoming dependent on the drug in the sense that he or she needs to continue taking it in order to function well, but this "dependency"—like that of a diabetic on insulin—is quite different from addiction. Sedative-hypnotic and antianxiety agents do have the potential for abuse; they should be prescribed judiciously, and patients should be monitored closely. However, if these medications are used as recommended, dependency usually will not be a problem.

Some patients object on philosophical grounds, contending that drugs are not "natural" and demand herbs or other agents which are "not chemical." Actually, the distinction between "chemical" and other psychoactive substances is purely arbitrary and based on an ignorance of chemistry. Everything we see around us is made up of chemicals. The air we breathe is made up of chemicals, the foods we eat (whether or not "organically grown") are made up of chemicals, and our very bodies are made up of chemicals. The fact that a psychiatric drug was produced in a laboratory instead of on a farm does not make it any "more" chemical. Indeed, many medications have been derived from plants or animals, and many common foods and beverages which are not regarded as drugs do contain psychoactive chemicals—for example, caffeine in coffee or certain soft drinks, alcohol in beer or wine. No matter how "natural" a substance may seem, it is still made of chemicals and exerts its influence through chemical reactions.

Some patients think that taking medications is a sign of weakness, an indication that he or she is unable to handle things without this "crutch." This argument ignores the fact that the patient has a problem which the medication is designed to alleviate. Just as crutches can help a person with a leg injury get about until the injury is healed, psychiatric medications can help a patient function better until normal functioning is possible without medications. The choice is not between being weak or being strong; it is between functioning well and functioning poorly until strength is regained.

An allied complaint is that the patient does not want his or her mind "taken over" by a drug. The fear of loss of control is understandable, but the fact is that, despite certain temporary effects, the drug will leave the patient basically the same person as before. Patients may complain that drugs interfere with thinking, but it is psychotic thinking which is meeting interference; far from "taking over" the patient's mind, the drug is returning rational control of the mind to the patient.

Yet another complaint is that medication is expensive. However, the expense of pills is a tremendous bargain when compared with the cost of staying in a hospital and losing time from work.

Other patients resist medication because they dislike and/or fear side effects. There is no question that some psychoactive drugs have undesirable side effects; however, this is not a reason to refuse to take any psychiatric medication. If side effects are experienced, they should be discussed with the psychiatrist, who usually will be able to adjust dosage so that side effects are not a major problem. In certain cases, it will be possible to prescribe an alternate medication which achieves the same desirable therapeutic effect with fewer or no undesirable side effects.

Finally, many patients who resist medication complain that it is having no effect or even that it is making the condition worse. Even when the patient honestly believes this, he or she is not always the best judge of a medication's effectiveness. Sometimes complaints of ineffectiveness are voiced even while it is clear to observers that the medication is producing day-to-day improvement. Some patients refuse to acknowledge improvement because they are resisting being treated; they protested at the onset that they did not need help, and, if they were to admit now that the treatment was working, they would be admitting that their earlier protestations were "wrong."

Not all psychiatric medications provide prompt relief. Antidepressants in particular take some time to work. The patient may well decide that the medication is not worth taking—especially if he or she has a history of drug abuse and has come to think of pills as being capable of eliminating uncomfortable feelings immediately.

You may understand better what the patient is experiencing by considering some typical case examples.

> A 32-year-old woman chronically used alcohol and tranquilizers to combat feelings of depression. Her dependency on these agents became a problem in itself and an obstacle in dealing with her depression.
>
> While hospitalized, she complained that antidepressant medication did not provide the relief she used to get from tranquilizers. She had difficulty accepting that the antidepressant medication might take three or four weeks to take effect.
>
> She repeatedly requested changes in her prescription, hoping to obtain some sedating effect. She complained of a variety of side effects rarely if ever associated with the drug she was taking. When she was unable to convince the psychiatrist to prescribe a different drug, she prevailed on relatives to smuggle tranquilizers into the hospital. On passes, she drank and used more tranquilizers.
>
> The psychiatrist suspected that something was amiss but had no evidence and was unable to do anything more than continue attempting treatment according to his original plan. Eventually the woman persuaded her family that she was not being helped at the hospital, and, on the family's insistence, she was discharged.
>
> Several months later she was readmitted after almost dying during an episode of heavy drinking and pill taking. The psychiatrist discussed the first period of hospitalization with members of

the family, and they confessed to the role they had played in interfering with her treatment. They promised full cooperation this time, and they warned the patient that they would have nothing further to do with her if she did not also cooperate.

Threatened, she became more motivated and participated in psychotherapy with less reluctance than before. She found that she was able to tolerate the mild side effects of her antidepressant medication, and, on schedule, the medication began to provide its customary relief. Meanwhile, her relatives enrolled in the hospital's family therapy program and learned not to play the role of "co-alcoholic," which encourages alcohol dependency.

Within a month, the woman was discharged. In follow-up visits, she showed evidence of recovery from her symptoms.

Depression, the most prevalent of mental disorders, can be relieved—at least temporarily—by alcohol, tranquilizers, or other agents. Unfortunately, the relief is illusory, because the feelings of depression return (often with greater intensity than before) after the drugs have been metabolized by the body. The patient then begins a vicious cycle of alcohol and drug abuse, requiring greater and greater quantities. The dependency on alcohol and tranquilizers becomes a second psychiatric problem, no less troublesome than the original problem of depression.

Whatever the patient's problem, it is essential that relatives recognize that a problem exists and cooperate in the treatment. If the family for one reason or another does not have faith in the psychiatrist, the best course of action is to seek help elsewhere—not to join with the patient to circumvent the psychiatrist's plan of treatment.

A 23-year-old man had come to believe that he was Jesus Christ. When people did not treat him as he thought they should treat the Savior, he quarreled with them and sometimes assaulted them. After one episode of assault, he was hospitalized.

He insisted that he had no problem other than the fact that people refused to recognize that he was The Chosen. Shortly after his intake interview, he attempted to leave the hospital. He assaulted the attendant who tried to restrain him.

The psychiatrist prescribed an antipsychotic drug to calm him. The patient insisted that he did not need it, and he refused to swallow the pill. When attendants demanded that he take the pill, he became very frightened and accused the hospital staff of trying to poison him. He thought he was fighting for his life, and six male staff members were required to place him in a bed with leather restraints.

He was given the antipsychotic medication by injection and within an hour was sufficiently calm to be released from the restraints. However, a short while later, when he was given additional medication, his tongue got stiff and started to stick out, and then his neck started twisting and his eyes rolled upward.

He was given another medicine, an antiparkinsonian drug, which made the symptoms disappear within fifteen minutes. However, he resisted future attempts at medication because he said he feared a recurrence of the earlier side effects.

Eventually he accepted medication by mouth only because he knew he would get it by injection if he refused. The side effects never recurred, and, within a short time, his condition had stabilized enough so that he was able to enter psychotherapy to deal with his problems.

When people experience a first psychotic episode, they have a psychological stake in resisting treatment. It is important for them to deny that they are having problems; if they were to admit that their perceptions are erroneous, they would be admitting, in effect, that their entire conception of the world is invalid.

In addition, their control over their lives has become jeopardized because they have not been able to function well due to their altered mental state. Relatives, friends, and even strangers seem to be taking control over them—first by disputing their perceptions, then (eventually) by placing them in a strange hospital environment. In this situation, the patient may fear complete loss of control when an attempt is made to administer a drug.

If the drug has side effects, the fear of loss of control is likely to intensify. However, side effects usually are not dangerous and in some instances can be overcome by a supplemental drug. For example, the specific muscle stiffness sometimes brought on by antipsychotic medications (as in this case) can be controlled by antiparkinsonian medications.

Given the patient's mental state on entering the hospital, his resistance to medication certainly was not surprising. All the same, while forced administration of a drug may seem callous or even brutal, the drug offers the best hope of bringing the psychotic episode—and the accompanying suffering—under control quickly.

A 27-year-old man had been hospitalized five times, the first at age 21. His symptoms included the delusion that there was a conspiracy against him and hallucinations of voices calling him derogatory names and threatening him.

During each period of hospitalization, he took the prescribed medications, and soon his symptoms went away. He would be discharged with instructions to continue taking the medications.

After a few follow-up visits, he would decide that he did not need the medications anymore and he would stop taking them. In a short time, the symptoms would return and he would be hospitalized once again.

He seemed unable to recognize the connection between taking his medicine and getting better and stopping the medication and eventually deteriorating again. The connection was clear to people around him, but he insisted that the only reason his problems were recurring was because people in the conspiracy had decided to interfere in his life once again.

When the threatening voices reappeared—usually four to five months after he had stopped taking his medications—he was afraid of them and initially would not tell his family that they had returned. His lifestyle would then become disorganized; he would dress sloppily, stop paying attention to his grooming, and ignore matters that clearly were in his interest such as maintaining contact with the welfare office that provided his disability payments.

His disorganization interfered with his outpatient therapy. He would fail to show up for appointments, sometimes saying that he had forgotten them, at other times saying he did not need help, and at still other times not bothering to explain at all.

During his fifth period of hospitalization, he displayed considerable hostility. His hallucinatory voices instructed him not to take medications. He told the psychiatrist that he was allergic to all psychiatric drugs—although this was not true and, even if it had been true, he would have had no way of knowing it was. When the drugs were administered over his protests, he complained of blurred vision and dizziness, although in truth he was not experiencing these side effects.

After being discharged from his fifth period of hospitalization, he appeared several times for outpatient therapy and then discontinued treatment again.

The "revolving door" syndrome of repeated hospitalization and discharge is quite common in schizophrenia. Although schizophrenic symptoms usually first come to professional attention with an acute episode, they often continue in a long-term pattern with recurring decompensations. Because of the nature of schizophrenia, patients may be unable to recognize the problem or understand that psychiatric intervention is warranted.

If a member of your family seems to fit this category, you should not regard the situation as hopeless. Even after years of resisting medication, patients may eventually come to recognize the value of the treatment. If a patient does not stop taking medication prematurely, the psychosis can be kept under control and the patient may not have to return to the hospital.

> *A 39-year-old woman—a highly successful clothing designer—had a history of bipolar disorder, in which manic states alternate with depressed states.*
>
> *When she was depressed, she was unable to work or even to care for herself. When she was hypomanic—that is, not fully manic—she functioned very well. At the extreme of her manic phase, she would become delusional and talk excitedly about celebrities who she mistakenly believed were involved in her life.*
>
> *Hospitalized, she initially cooperated with the psychiatrist's prescription of lithium, the usual medication for mania. However, when she found that the drug eliminated her extremely productive hypomanic phase (as well as her deep depressions and delusional manic episodes), she refused to take it.*

Resistance to lithium therapy is not uncommon. Although many patients are delighted to obtain stability of mood, others are willing to pay the price of deep depression and delusional mania in order to continue experiencing the desired manic or hypomanic periods.

This same sort of trade-off explains, to an extent, the resistance of alcoholics and drug abusers to corrective medication: the desirable "high" is regarded as just too important to forgo, no matter what the price.

> *A 44-year-old woman had consulted many practitioners about recurring episodes of depression.*
>
> *An orthomolecular doctor said she should use only vitamins. A chiropractor maintained that her problems were caused by a pinched nerve. A nutritionist insisted that the problems could be solved by the proper diet.*
>
> *She then consulted three psychiatrists. The first prescribed lithium, the second antidepressants, and the third antipsychotics.*

Hospitalized, she was understandably skeptical about the entire mental health field. Even though she did not know about the differences among the drugs prescribed by her last three doctors, she certainly knew that she received an extraordinary array of diverse and sometimes conflicting advice from the first five people she consulted.

She was extremely hostile during her initial interview, and her hostility might be seen as a natural reaction to her frustration with earlier practitioners. However, as the interview continued, the psychiatrist could see that the woman had personality problems predating her series of attempts at getting help for her depression. In fact, she had begun quarreling with all of her therapists early in the relationships and had quit before any of the prescribed treatments might have had a chance to work.

The hospital psychiatrist prescribed medication but after a few days, the woman insisted on being discharged.

This woman, like many other people who visit a variety of therapists, was told something different by virtually everyone she consulted. Patients who try several medications or other treatments without success are likely to have doubts about the next medication or treatment and may resist it, especially if side effects are unpleasant.

This is unfortunate, because not all psychiatric medications work instantaneously. Antidepressants may not show their full effect for several weeks. Other psychiatric drugs, such as antipsychotics, may take at least a few days to produce good results. If the medication is not given a fair trial, it will seem ineffective and the patient will have further reason to doubt the effectiveness of any psychiatric medication.

HOW YOU CAN HELP

As the relative of any patient—psychiatric or not—you can make an extremely important contribution to the patient's recovery by familiarizing yourself with the medications that have been prescribed and by helping the patient take them according to instructions.

Most people who are seriously ill, whatever the illness, are not as alert as when they were in perfect health. In their stressed condition, they may become forgetful, unmotivated, or even irrational.

For example, a cancer patient who is undergoing chemotherapy may be fully aware of the importance of taking medications on a certain schedule. However, the patient may become preoccupied and forget to take the pills—or, equally dangerously, may take them and forget having done so, then take them again.

Sometimes a simple system, initiated at the suggestion of a relative, can solve this problem without inconveniencing anyone and without making the patient feel childish or dependent. For example, if a pill is to be taken every six hours, it's a good idea to put aside the day's supply of four pills at the beginning of the day. You might put them in a small dish, a glass, or any other convenient receptacle. If a pill is not taken on schedule, it will remain in the receptacle, and you can see when it has not been taken.

If you have any doubt about the patient's motivation or ability to keep track of pill-taking, it might be a good idea to be present when the pill is being taken. You might even devise a sort of ritual in which you have a glass of water or some other beverage when the patient takes the pill. Cooperatively sharing the patient's schedule can ensure that the schedule is maintained.

Let me repeat that familial support can be valuable to any person who is seriously ill. However, it can be especially valuable to the psychiatric outpatient, who may have a great many reasons for resisting medication.

Here is my program for relatives who want to provide the greatest possible support and assistance during a regimen of psychiatric medication.

In The Hospital

In previous chapters we discussed your relationship with the psychiatrist and how to work together cooperatively to determine what role you should play in treatment. This is especially important when it comes to medications. You normally will not be present when medications are taken, but you can help ensure that the patient is aware of their value and the importance of taking them as prescribed.

First, discuss the plan of treatment with the psychiatrist. Learn which drugs have been chosen, what results they are likely to produce, and which side effects (if any) the patient might experience. The psychiatrist probably will have discussed these matters with the patient, but some patients—whether because of preoccupation, poor attention span, lack of motivation, resistance, or some other factor—

may not understand or remember what the psychiatrist said.

If you have any doubts about the plan of treatment, express them. This is not to say that you should second-guess the psychiatrist. But it is important for you to know exactly what the psychiatrist has in mind for your relative and to believe that the approach is prudent. The psychiatrist's answers to your questions should put your mind at ease. If you are not satisfied, you may want to consider making other arrangements for the care of your relative. In the event that you are satisfied, you will be equipped to help your relative understand the importance of cooperating.

When discussing medications with the psychiatrist, it is important to provide complete information about the patient's medical history and any drugs the patient may have taken before being hospitalized. This information can be extremely valuable, helping the psychiatrist to make an accurate diagnosis and decide which medications to use.

For example, if the patient has been treated for diabetes or some other endocrine disorder, that disorder, or the treatment of it, may help explain certain psychiatric signs and symptoms. Likewise, if the patient has been taking certain medications for blood pressure problems, there could be a danger in prescribing certain psychiatric medications. If the patient has been using "street drugs," sleeping pills, tranquilizers, or alcohol, the information can be of both diagnostic and therapeutic value.

The psychiatrist most probably will have discussed these matters with the patient, but the patient may not have revealed the truth. If a patient is delusional, it is especially important for the psychiatrist to get information from the family.

During your discussion with the psychiatrist, ask also about drugs, foods, and beverages that should not be taken at the same time as the prescribed medication. Alcohol, for example, can cause unexpectedly great sedation in combination with certain medications.

There is very little likelihood that your relative will receive any food, beverage, or drug from hospital personnel that will interfere with his or her medication, but he or she may receive something dangerous from other patients—for example, a "street drug" that a visitor may have brought to a patient. Your relative may be motivated to disobey rules or simply be lacking in judgment and take the drug. You can impress your relative with the importance of following the psychiatrist's instructions—pointing out that anything which interferes with medication can delay recovery and prolong hospitalization.

Your relative may ask you to smuggle alcohol or drugs into the hospital. My warning against cooperating with such a request may seem unnecessary, but the fact is that sometimes patients persuade relatives to do exactly that. For example, patients who have abused antianxiety agents may complain of extraordinary tension and nervousness in the hospital. They may say they cannot stand living this way. They may express the fear that they will go completely crazy if they do not get some relief. They may further say that they have asked for a prescription and the psychiatrist refused.

You may be sure that if a prescription was refused, it was refused for a good reason. The requested drug may be one which interacts with the prescribed medication. Or dependency on this or similar drugs may be one of the major problems which the psychiatrist's plan of treatment is designed to overcome.

The more you know about the plan of treatment, the better equipped you will be to assist in your relative's recovery. Once you yourself have become convinced of the benefits of the medications, you can help convince the patient of the importance of taking them. You can also explain why medications may not be working immediately, and you can reassure your relative when undesired side effects are only temporary. The psychiatrist almost certainly will have done this, but your relative may be more accepting of the situation if you reinforce the psychiatrist's explanation.

None of the above is to say that you and the psychiatrist should "gang up" on the patient. However, a treatment plan that is not followed will not work. If you are not convinced that the psychiatrist is doing the right thing for your relative, ask questions until you become convinced or decide to seek treatment elsewhere. Once you are convinced, do your best to convince the patient. If the patient is satisfied that a supportive relative has assessed the situation intelligently, the patient is much more likely to cooperate—and to recover more quickly.

Sometimes a patient who objects to medication may want a relative to try to persuade the psychiatrist to change the treatment. Many patients will complain that the treatment is not working or that the side effects are unbearable. Some, eager to leave the hospital, will exaggerate symptoms or even fabricate stories about side effects, uncomfortable living conditions, or abuses by members of the staff. Some will attempt to exploit a relative's sensitivities to guilt, pity, or protectiveness.

By all means, listen sympathetically to the patient's complaints. If you feel they are unwarranted, explain your reasoning. If you feel they are justified, discuss them with the psychiatrist. This is not to say that you should be a referee in disputes that the patient may have with the psychiatrist or other members of the staff. However, as an intermediary, you can help both the psychiatrist and the patient— and, in the process, contribute greatly to a speedy recovery.

After Hospitalization

Discuss with the psychiatrist whether you should keep in touch, come to appointments, or leave reporting of symptoms up to the patient.

If the psychiatrist wants you to be actively involved in treatment after the patient has been discharged to outpatient therapy, your help may become even more important than it was in the hospital.

Now there will be no nurses to ensure that medications are taken on schedule or to watch for side effects or complications. The patient will have been told what to expect, but a second pair of eyes can be extremely valuable.

For example, in lithium therapy, the blood level must be monitored carefully. The level can be affected by changes in body water and salts. Excessive sweating or diarrhea can cause such changes. The psychiatrist should be notified immediately, because lithium toxicity can be fatal.

Often patients stop taking their medication, drop out of treatment, get worse, and must return to the hospital. Deterioration may not be noticeable for months, but by then the patient may absolutely refuse medication. It is usually much easier to encourage a patient to keep taking medication than to start over again.

It is very important for relatives and friends to keep close watch on a seriously depressed patient who may be suicidal. You know the patient much better than the psychiatrist does. You may notice changes which the psychiatrist cannot observe during outpatient consultations—or you may observe changes which develop between consultations.

By being available and providing emotional support, you can help the patient overcome depressive episodes. If you suspect that the patient may be considering suicide, contact the psychiatrist immediately.

The psychiatrist may ask you not to actively participate in the therapy relationship or may want you to work along closely for as long as outpatient therapy continues. If you are to be closely involved, discuss, as you did when the patient was hospitalized, exactly what is happening and why. Also, discuss the patient's progress and the psychiatrist's expectations.

After outpatient therapy has ended, you might continue to monitor the patient's behavior. You may be the first to notice that a condition is recurring or that some other problem is developing. If treatment is not sought promptly, the situation may get much worse very rapidly.

None of this is to say that you should take responsibility for running your relative's life. As I have stated more than once in this book, the primary goal of psychiatric treatment is to help the patient become completely independent as quickly as possible. However, without your help, the process may take much longer.

8

Psychiatric Medications:
Specific Drugs

There are dozens of psychiatric medications that have been introduced over the past several decades, and new ones are being developed
all the time. This chapter will cover the agents that are most widely
used in psychiatric hospitals today.

SEDATIVE-HYPNOTICS
AND ANTIANXIETY AGENTS

Drugs in this group have differences in biochemical action as well as
in effect, but they also have significant similarities. Often one can be
substituted for another with more or less the same results. At
properly adjusted doses they all cause drowsiness, and they all help
calm nervousness. (Hypnotics—described colloquially as "sleeping
pills"—cause more drowsiness, while sedatives and antianxiety
agents encourage a greater degree of relaxation in a waking state.)

Along with their other commonalities, these categories of drugs
have potential for abuse and can cause physical dependence. People
can develop a "tolerance" to them—that is, begin to need higher and
higher doses to get the same effect. Sometimes a person becomes so

dependent that it becomes necessary to stop the medication slowly, with decreasing doses over a period of time in order to avoid discomfort or even medically dangerous conditions during withdrawal. (This is the only category of medications described in this chapter that are habit-forming in this sense.)

For a familiar example of how sedative-hypnotics and antianxiety agents cause problems at the same time that they make people feel better, we can look at alcohol, which operates in much the same way. Many people, finding that it "calms their nerves," use it to relax in social situations. Some people use it to escape more serious anxiety or deeper psychological problems. It also can help a person fall asleep more easily.

Unfortunately, a person who has trouble sleeping may suffer psychological problems, such as depression, or certain medical problems. Using alcohol or some drug to knock oneself out is bad treatment because it does not deal with the underlying problem. It is far better to treat the problem than the symptom.

A person can develop a tolerance to alcohol. Then, when the person stops drinking there are withdrawal symptoms, such as tremors, nausea, anxiety, or even—in advanced cases—hallucinations or seizures.

Not insignificantly, a patient in alcohol withdrawal may be given a sedative-hypnotic or antianxiety agent to ease these symptoms. The drugs work because of the similarity between them and alcohol. (Persons having withdrawal problems with sedative-hypnotics or antianxiety agents may be given a different drug within this group—in decreasing doses—to prevent complications or other problems.)

Over-the-counter sedatives are extensively advertised and widely used. They are not as strong as prescription drugs, and it is difficult to tell how much of the effect is a result of " placebo," or mind-over-matter—that is, the person who takes them is convinced that they will work and believes that they are working.

A number of prescription drugs also are used as hypnotics. Chloral hydrate, sold under several brand names (for example, Noctec), is the oldest and still very widely used. Another old one is paraldehyde, widely employed at one time to alleviate alcohol withdrawal and disturbed behavior in some psychiatric conditions; it is not used as frequently now because it has an objectionable smell and because other drugs have become available.

Some drugs in this category must be used very carefully because they can be addicting and because in overdose they can be deadly. The better-known ones include (trade names are followed parenthetically by chemical names) Quaalude (methaqualone), Doriden (glutethimide), and Noludar (methyprylon). Barbiturates, which all have a similar chemical makeup, are also sedative-hypnotics; they include Luminal (phenobarbital), Amytal (amobarbital), Nembutal (pentobarbital), Seconal (secobarbital), Brevital (methohexital), and Pentothal (thiopental). Dalmane (flurazepam) is chemically similar to the antianxiety agents, and may be safer in regard to overdose.

A serious problem with hypnotics, as with alcohol when used as a sleep-inducer, is interference with the normal sleep pattern. A person may find the drugs very helpful in inducing sleep, but the quality of sleep is not as good as the person would get without the drug.

Antianxiety agents and sedatives can also help induce sleep, although they usually are prescribed primarily to allay anxiety or other conditions colloquially described as nervousness. Unfortunately, as with hypnotics, patients can develop a tolerance to them that diminishes the medications' ability to sedate.

The best-known antianxiety agents (also known as "minor tranquilizers") include Valium (diazepam), Librium (chlordiazepoxide), and Miltown, Equanil, or Meprospan (all brand names of meprobamate). Other drugs in this class include Serax (oxazepam), Tranxene (clorazepate), Ativan (lorazepam), and Vistaril or Atarax (hydroxyzine). These drugs all have different chemical structures and differences in their effects (for example, how long they are effective) but they all are in many ways very similar.

If drugs in this group are prescribed for your relative, you should watch for their side effects. The drugs—sedative-hypnotics and antianxiety agents—can cause drowsiness, so the patient must take care not to drive an automobile or engage in other activities that require an alert mind. Moreover, the drugs' effects can be magnified if other drugs or alcohol are used at the same time. The result can be unexpectedly great sedation or even death. In fact, many people have died because they consumed alcoholic beverages in large quantities together with sedatives or antianxiety agents.

Other side effects of drugs in this group include hangovers, which may occur just as with alcohol. As with many other drugs, there also is the possibility of congenital abnormalities resulting from use during pregnancy, although evidence thus far is inconclusive.

Given that there is a high percentage of depressives among people who use these drugs, the user's potential for suicide cannot be overlooked. As a matter of fact, taking an overdose of sleeping pills is one of the most common methods of suicide.

ANTIPSYCHOTIC AGENTS

Some years ago, when psychoactive medications were in their infancy, the term "tranquilizer" came into vogue to describe agents whose action was sedating (that is, drugs that made people feel "tranquil"). A distinction was made between "minor tranquilizers," the antianxiety agents described above, and "major tranquilizers," a different category of drug employed principally among patients with certain severe emotional disturbances. The latter category of drugs also is called "neuroleptic."

One problem with the designations "minor tranquilizers" and "major tranquilizers" is that they invite the inference that the drugs are very similar. In fact, they are quite different in their effects as well as in their biochemical action.

Antipsychotic medications were developed in the 1950s, and their use rapidly became widespread, with dramatic results. Suddenly psychiatrists were able to bring about significant improvement in patients who previously were impervious to treatment. In a majority of cases, patients were able to live less disturbed, if not actually productive, lives.

Some of the most commonly used drugs in this category are Thorazine (chlorpromazine), Compazine (prochlorperazine), Trilafon (perphenazine), Stelazine (trifluoperazine), Prolixin or Permitil (fluphenazine), Mellaril (thioridazine), Haldol (haloperidol), Navane (thiothixene), Loxitane (loxapine), and Moban or Lidone (molindone), but there are also many other antipsychotic agents. These drugs act selectively on certain areas of the brain, causing tiny biochemical changes that in turn cause changes in the functioning of the nervous system. Exactly how all this works is still not completely understood, but there is no question that the medications can be very effective.

With antipsychotic drugs, as with other medications, side effects are common. The drugs often cause uncomfortable feelings, especially at the beginning of a course of therapy, and in certain circumstances they can be dangerous. However, the widespread worry about side effects from psychiatric drugs in general and antipsychotic medications in particular is not justified by the low incidence of serious problems related to these drugs. Some patients who object to being treated altogether may claim that they do not have a psychiatric problem and are being given medication against their will for unsound reasons. Actually, if dosages are properly adjusted and additional medications are used appropriately, truly bothersome side effects usually can be eliminated.

Sometimes a patient will have a problem with one psychiatric medication and subsequently resist all psychiatric medications. Actually, even if the same medication is used on a later occasion, there is a good chance that bothersome side effects can be eliminated or at least controlled. In many cases, simply explaining how to deal with a reaction that a patient has suffered will help prevent it from happening again. Probably the most bothersome aspect of side effects for some patients is the fact that certain strange feelings (ranging from dizziness to dryness of the mouth) occur unexpectedly.

Patients sometimes say that they are allergic to medication in an effort to persuade the psychiatrist not to prescribe it for them. Actually, most such patients are not allergic. Allergies may occur with antipsychotic drugs as with penicillin or many other medications, but not all side effects are allergic reactions. The term "allergy" refers to a specific kind of reaction of the body to a foreign substance, such as plant pollens or certain foods. The foreign substance, called an "antigen," stimulates the body to produce other substances, called "antibodies," and the allergic reaction may include such symptoms as sneezing, rash, respiratory problems, or even more serious disturbances (such as shock). The body's special active response mechanism for an allergic reaction is different from most of the side effects seen with antipsychotic medications. The latter usually are caused by the direct effect of the drug on the nervous system or on other parts of the body.

It is important to distinguish between allergic reactions and other, more common types of side effects. Allergy may really mean that a specific medication should be avoided, while side effects are very common and usually are much less troublesome than the psychiatric disorder being treated.

Probably the most frequent side effect of antipsychotic medications is drowsiness. This may be most noticeable during the first few days of treatment, when the patient is most disturbed, when the body has not yet had a chance to get used to the medication, and when the dosage is being adjusted. Drowsiness is not a major problem and may even be helpful if the patient is being tormented by hallucinations or delusions or is potentially dangerous. By the time of the patient's discharge from the hospital, the dosage generally will have been adjusted to a level where drowsiness is not troublesome. Of course, if the patient is even slightly drowsy, he or she should not drive or operate machinery or engage in other activities that require total alertness.

Other side effects are called "autonomic," because they relate to bodily activities controlled by the autonomic nervous system. This system controls such "automatic" functions as focusing your eyes, regulating your heart rate and blood pressure, determining the amount of saliva in your mouth, and regulating contractions in your stomach and intestines. As you can imagine, this sort of nervous system control is different from the voluntary control you exercise when you move your arms, legs, or other parts of the body. Many psychiatric drugs create temporary imbalance of the autonomic nervous system, and the accompanying side effects may include dryness of the mouth, constipation, blurred vision, or dizziness.

Dryness of the mouth can be unpleasant, but it often decreases after medication has been used for a few days. The dryness is not caused by dehydration or lack of water in the body but by the failure of the salivary glands to produce saliva as usual. Many patients get relief by drinking extra water or eating candy or chewing gum to stimulate salivation. (If the patient chews gum, it should be a sugarless kind, for cavities form more easily in a dry mouth when sugar is present.)

Constipation is a common side effect which usually does not become a major problem, but it should always be called to the doctor's attention. The usual treatment is a mild laxative, such as milk of magnesia, or, if this does not work, an enema. Or a stool softener such as Colace (docusate sodium) may be used.

Blurred vision sometimes occurs as a result of interference with the eyes' focusing mechanism. The patient can see clearly at a distance but has difficulty with close vision. It may be necessary to hold a newspaper or other reading material farther from the eyes than usual in order to see it clearly. There is no need to treat this; the eyes should return to normal when the medication is discontinued (unless there is some other cause of blurred vision, such as the need for eyeglasses).

Dizziness may occur when a person stands quickly after sitting or lying, and it usually lasts for only a few seconds. The reaction, termed "orthostatic hypotension," is explained by interference with the autonomic mechanism that regulates flow of blood. When a person is lying, and to a somewhat lesser extent when he or she is sitting, blood is pumped through the body more freely than when the person is standing and gravity tends to pull the blood away from the head and toward the feet. Thus, when a person is standing, the heart and blood vessels must provide more pressure to keep the brain supplied with blood. When a person stands abruptly, the body must adjust the pressure of the blood, or there will be dizziness and perhaps also faintness. This lasts for only a few seconds, so the side effect is not as bad as it may sound. In any event, the solution is simply to rise very slowly, allowing the autonomic mechanism more time to adjust.

There are other, less common autonomic side effects, and some of the more unusual ones—such as markedly impaired movement of the intestines—can be dangerous, so every side effect should be reported to the psychiatrist.

Another category of side effects is termed "extrapyramidal" because they involve nerves that fall outside (thus, "extra") a pyramid-shaped part of the nervous system's anatomy.

One of the most uncomfortable—and frightening—of the extrapyramidal side effects (or "EPS") is acute dystonic reaction, in which there is a sudden onset of such symptoms as stiffness and protrusion of the tongue, tightening and twisting of the neck, inability to keep the eyes from rolling upward, and arching of the back and neck. Some patients may fear that they are dying even though death is not a real danger. Actually, the reaction can be eliminated fairly quickly if the patient is given an intramuscular injection of Cogentin (benztropine) or some similar agent from a group of medications known as "antiparkinsonian" (because they are used to treat Parkinson's disease). In fact, some psychiatrists routinely prescribe an oral dosage of one of these medications along with the antipsychotic drug as a way of preventing the reaction from occurring; however, other psychiatrists believe that antiparkinsonian drugs may add problems, such as additional side effects, so they do not prescribe the two together routinely. The matter is the subject of research at present.

Acute dystonic reaction usually occurs early in treatment, so the likelihood is that the patient will be in the hospital at the time and will receive prompt attention. If the patient is not in the hospital, he or she should be taken to the emergency room of the nearest hospital. The staff should be told that the patient is taking an antipsychotic medication. In the unlikely event that the reaction occurs when the patient is alone and unable to summon help, and if the patient does not have access to Cogentin or some similarly effective drug, such as Artane (trihexyphenidyl) or Benadryl (diphenhydramine), the reaction will go away on its own. Needless to say, the experience may be distressing for the patient, and it is extremely unfortunate that the reaction occurs, but the value of the antipsychotic medication is considered sufficiently high to warrant the relatively low risk of the reaction.

A second type of extrapyramidal effect is Parkinsonian syndrome, which produces symptoms similar to those of Parkinson's disease: a flat, emotionless facial expression; shuffling gait; tremor, especially of the hands; and general stiffness and slowness of movement. These symptoms also can be controlled with Cogentin, Artane, and similar agents.

A third type of extrapyramidal side effect, called "akathisia," takes the form of persistent restlessness. The patient feels the desire to walk about constantly and cannot be comfortable sitting or lying. Once again, Cogentin, Artane, and similar agents can overcome the reaction.

These three types of extrapyramidal side effects occur only while the antipsychotic medication is being taken. Thus, there is generally no need to fear that they will recur after the psychiatrist has taken the patient off the medication.

Unfortunately, a fourth type of extrapyramidal side effect, called "tardive dyskinesia," is not so easily manageable. It usually does not appear unless medication has been used in high doses for quite some time. It occurs when dosage of the medication is being decreased or after the medication has been discontinued. Its symptoms may include chewing-like movements of the mouth and tongue, lip smacking, grimaces, abnormal grunting during respiration, and twisting movements in the fingers and feet.

There is at present no known cure for these symptoms. Sometimes they will go away on their own, but in other cases they will remain. Obviously, the risk of this side effect must be considered when antipsychotic medication is prescribed, particularly for long periods with chronic patients. Yet, despite the dangers, it may still be preferable to use the medication if that means keeping the patient out of the hospital and free of the more severe symptoms of psychosis. Fortunately, tardive dyskinesia generally occurs only when heavy dosages of antipsychotic medication have been used for a long time.

Other temporary side effects may occur. For example, the skin may become more susceptible to sunburn, the breasts may become engorged and produce milk, and some male patients may become sexually impotent. I stress that these side effects are temporary; in most cases they will go away when the medication has been changed or discontinued.

There may be permanent side effects, also, such as changes in the pigment of the skin or within the eye. Most such problems are not serious, but in extremely rare cases may cause serious disability or even death. Once again, these risks must be weighed against the possible benefits when medication is used.

Another point must be made: although all the symptoms discussed may appear as side effects to antipsychotic medications, they may also have other causes. So you should not assume that just because the symptoms appear, the medicine is responsible. Indeed, a problem in diagnosis is that certain symptoms—for example, emotional withdrawal, restlessness, or strange facial movements—can also be symptoms of the psychosis that the medicine is supposed to treat. Thus, the psychiatrist must determine what is causing the symptom and whether the solution is more medication rather than less.

Whatever side effects your relative experiences, the psychiatrist should be told about them. In the majority of cases, an adjustment in the dosage or even the passage of time will eliminate the problem or at least reduce the severity of the symptom. At the same time, a patient's complaints about side effects must be weighed judiciously, because many patients complain of symptoms that are not associated with the medications they are taking. For example, some patients insist that their medication is causing hallucinations when the hallucinations existed before the patient began taking medication.

ANTIDEPRESSANTS

Antidepressant drugs combat depression through biochemical changes in the brain. No one knows for sure yet exactly how this happens, but the empirical evidence is conclusive that it does happen. Not all patients show dramatic improvement, but the majority experience significant relief.

Unfortunately, unlike most drugs, antidepressants take a long time to produce their effect. Sometimes they will show results within a few days, but often the patient must use them for three to four weeks before the full effect is achieved. Occasional use on an "as needed" basis simply will not work.

The most commonly used class of antidepressants is the tricyclics, so called because there are three rings, or "cycles," in their chemical structure. Their antidepressant effect was discovered by accident. During a search for new antipsychotic medications, a drug was found that did not help psychosis but did produce a significant improvement in the mood of depressed patients. Researchers continue to search for the exact answer to why this effect occurs; meanwhile, the tricyclics have brought unmeasurable relief to many patients.

Some long-established medications in this category are Tofranil (imipramine), Elavil (amitriptyline), Norpramin or Pertofrane (desipramine), Aventyl or Pamelor (nortriptyline), Sinequan or Adapin (doxepin), and Vivactil (protriptyline). More recently developed agents include another tricyclic, Asendin (amoxapine) and two other antidepressants, Desyrel (trazodone) and Ludiomil (maprotiline), which are not tricyclics but have similar effects.

Perhaps the most common side effects of these medications are categorized as autonomic—that is, they relate to bodily activities controlled by the autonomic nervous system. The side effects include dryness of the mouth, constipation, blurred vision, and dizziness.

Other kinds of problems may arise. Drowsiness is a common side effect. Adjustments in dosage can help, but sometimes sedation is welcomed for calming nervousness or as an aid to getting a good night's sleep—often a problem for depressed patients.

A more worrisome problem can be the antidepressant's effect on the heart if an overdose is taken. It is important to be alert to this possibility, because some depressed patients are suicidal. Sometimes a few weeks' supply of antidepressants taken all at once can be fatal. Psychiatrists can guard against this possibility by prescribing in small quantities, but an extra measure of caution never hurts, and you can contribute greatly to your relative's well-being by helping to monitor his or her supply of antidepressants, especially if he or she expresses suicidal thoughts.

Other side effects are more annoying than dangerous, such as rash and tremor. They usually can be eliminated by a change in dosage or in the specific medication within the tricyclic class. Once again, all symptoms should be reported to the psychiatrist.

The second class of antidepressants is called "MAO inhibitors" because these agents work by inhibiting the enzyme monoamine oxidase (MAO). They are less widely used than the tricyclics because, among other reasons, they can cause high blood pressure, which can be dangerous. This reaction may occur after the patient has eaten certain foods. Thus, if MAO inhibitors are used, the psychiatrist will probably provide certain diet instructions. You can help by making sure that the patient follows these instructions.

In addition to relieving depression, some antidepressant medications may be helpful for certain types of panic attacks and phobias. These attacks usually arise when a person is alone, and there is separation from supportive people and reassuring places. Anxiety may occur in tunnels, on bridges, or on public transportation. Panic may include feelings of terror and helplessness, rapid heartbeat, sweating, faintness, trembling, a sensation of choking or smothering, and fear of dying or going crazy.

LITHIUM

Mania, which alternates with depression in the bipolar disorder discussed in Chapter Five, used to be treated with tranquilizers. However, since 1970, lithium (a chemical element similar to sodium and potassium) has been the preferred treatment. It is given in the form of a salt, lithium carbonate (just as sodium is ingested most commonly in the form of everyday table salt, sodium chloride). About a week or so usually elapses before an adequate level of lithium stabilizes in the patient's body and the manic mood is brought under control. Antipsychotic medications may be administered concurrently until the lithium takes effect and sometimes for longer periods.

Lithium is extremely effective, but it can be dangerous if too much is present in the body. The level must be very carefully adjusted, and you, as the patient's relative, may be asked to help monitor the chemical's use. Normally this is done at a laboratory, where blood samples are taken and the level of lithium is measured. However, you can get an indication that the level is too high by watching for certain side effects.

Early side effects include shakiness of the hands, mild thirst and nausea, and more urination than is usual. These are typical side effects and are not evidence that the lithium level is dangerously high.

However, diarrhea, vomiting, drowsiness, and muscular weakness or incoordination are danger signs. They do not necessarily mean that the lithium level is getting dangerously high, but this is a possibility, and the psychiatrist should be informed of the symptoms at once.

An overly high level of lithium may result from one of several problems. The dosage may be too high, or the body may be excreting less than the normal amount of lithium during urination, or there may be a deficiency in the total amount of body water available to dilute the lithium (as a result, for example, of sweating or diarrhea). Should any of these circumstances arise, it may be necessary to decrease the dosage or discontinue the medication. If this is not done, additional symptoms may develop: worse vomiting and diarrhea, muscular shakiness, incoordination, sluggishness, slurred speech, blurred vision, ringing in the ears, and much more urination than usual. Should any of these side effects occur, notify the psychiatrist immediately. If the body's imbalance of lithium is not corrected, the patient may die.

Other side effects of lithium therapy may include thinning of the hair and thyroid malfunction. Changes in kidney structure and function also have been reported.

Obviously, given the many hazards, lithium must be used very carefully, and a decision to employ the drug on a long-term basis is not made lightly. However, the benefits are also great if lithium conquers a manic condition and helps a person stay out of the hospital. There is a probable genetic and biochemical involvement in bipolar disorder, and there is great likelihood that once mania has occurred it will occur again. Lithium often is recommended to prevent future occurrences.

Lithium became familiar to the general public fairly quickly through magazine articles and television programs that hailed it as a wonder drug. But it is not a cure-all, so do not feel disappointed if you ask about using it and your relative's psychiatrist says it is not appropriate.

ANTABUSE

Antabuse (disulfiram) is different from the other drugs in this chapter because it does not act directly on the brain, but it is included here because it can be helpful in the treatment of alcoholism. It interferes with the chemical reaction that the body uses to break down and excrete alcohol. This interference creates a chemical, called acetaldehyde, which makes a person feel sick.

If you drink even a small amount of alcohol while you are taking Antabuse, your reactions may include sweating, thirst, a throbbing headache, a feeling of warmth, nausea and vomiting, difficulty breathing, rapid heartbeat, chest pain, weakness, and dizziness. Not surprisingly, someone who experiences these symptoms is likely to stay away from alcohol. And that is how Antabuse works, rather than by eliminating or diminishing the appetite for alcohol.

If a person is strongly motivated to stop drinking, Antabuse can be a last line of defense that keeps the person from "falling off the wagon;" however, if a person does not really want to stop, he or she may stop taking the medication. You can help by making sure that the schedule of dosage is being maintained.

There are usually no significant side effects to Antabuse if a person does not drink. However, it is imperative that the person does not ingest alcohol in any form. This means not eating foods with alcohol in them, not using cough mixtures that contain alcohol, and not ingesting alcohol in any other way.

If a doctor decides that a patient will have difficulty understanding the importance of not drinking while taking Antabuse, he or she might not prescribe the drug, no matter how serious a problem the patient's alcoholism may be.

PSYCHOMOTOR STIMULANTS

Certain stimulant drugs are used to treat attention deficit disorder. There is debate about the nature and cause of the disorder, but it seems fairly clear that children who are easily distracted have difficulty mastering academic subjects in school and learning the skills that they need in order to get along with their peers. Failure to learn these skills at an early age may lead to serious problems later on. Stimulants such as Cylert (pemoline), Dexedrine (dextroamphetamine), and Ritalin (methylphenidate) often help.

Once again, the pros and cons of using medication must be weighed. It may be hard for parents to accept that a child might benefit from taking a psychoactive drug regularly. However, these drugs have produced excellent results in many cases.

Occasional side effects include loss of appetite and difficulty sleeping. These disturbances usually can be eliminated by adjusting the dosage or changing the time of day that the medicine is taken. There is also some concern about whether these agents may inhibit growth.

Some people worry about addiction or psychosis as a result of taking the drugs. However, although stimulants may cause addiction or psychosis, this generally does not seem to happen among children. Also, even though stimulants can cause a "high" among adults and often are used for staying awake or losing weight, these effects generally are not seen among children. In fact it is precisely the opposite effect—a calming and settling effect—that makes these drugs useful among children with attention deficit disorder.

9

Other Psychiatric Therapies

Most treatment at today's psychiatric hospitals is limited to medications, psychotherapy, and such psychotherapy-related programs as
milieu therapy and activity therapy (described in an earlier chapter).
However, there are several other approaches that may be found in
certain hospitals.

ELECTROCONVULSIVE TREATMENT

Electroconvulsive treatment (ECT), also described as "electroshock"
or "shock therapy," has a long history and (unfortunately) an
unfavorable image. It is thought of as cruel and painful, and charges
have long been made that it is overused, especially in state hospitals.

All of this must be viewed in perspective. Not so long ago, there
was no effective treatment for mental illness, and any therapy that
offered promise was greeted with excitement. It was noted that when
certain patients recovered from spontaneous convulsions, their mental problems had abated somewhat. Thus, like antidepressants and
other later-day medications that proved their worth empirically even
though their exact mechanism of action remains unknown, induc-

ing convulsions with drugs became an accepted therapy.

Not too long afterward, clinicians found that the same effect could be better achieved by stimulating the convulsion electrically. A stimulus was applied to the head to initiate the seizure, and later, patients displayed the same sort of improvement that they had after a drug-induced convulsion.

In the early days, the patient was bound to a table with straps while the electrical stimulus was applied. The body would thrash about and there often were broken bones or other injuries. Today, in the places that employ electroconvulsive therapy, the situation is quite different. A drug, succinylcholine, is administered to relax the muscles so that they do not contract during a treatment. The effect of the stimulus on the brain remains the same, but the body hardly moves. The patient is also given a short-acting barbiturate that makes him or her fall asleep before the succinylcholine and electroshock are given. As a result, the patient sleeps quietly through the procedure. On waking a few minutes later, he or she will experience confusion for a brief period.

Treatments are usually given in series, and the number varies from case to case. After several treatments, patients normally show some loss of memory, but this generally disappears after the series is completed. There is some question in certain cases about how much loss of memory patients may experience. However, there is no question that ECT is extremely helpful to people with certain psychiatric problems, especially certain types of depression, and that some patients get better with ECT even when they have failed to improve with antidepressant medications and all other attempts at therapy.

In recent years, there has been considerable activity by groups that are opposed philosophically to the use of ECT, and many hospitals now provide formal review and informed consent procedures before ECT is employed. While this activism has satisfied some peoples' goals of restricting the use of ECT, it has also meant that some patients can not obtain the treatment even when it seems to offer the best hope for improvement.

If ECT is recommended for your relative, at least consider the possible benefits, which may turn out to weigh more heavily than the risks. Discuss the pros and cons with the psychiatrist, and try to keep an open mind.

Should your relative undergo ECT, you can play a vital role

immediately afterward by giving the patient support and attention, both of which are very important during the period of memory loss and confusion.

PSYCHOSURGERY

Psychosurgery is another procedure that was greeted with considerable excitement decades ago. It was introduced in the 1930s, before medications were available to relieve distressing mental conditions. The most popular surgical procedure was prefrontal lobotomy, in which the front part of the brain was separated surgically from the rest of the brain; this often stopped unmanageable patients from being assaultive.

Psychosurgery is rarely used today. Medications have supplanted psychosurgery except in the most extraordinary cases. It is highly unlikely that you ever will be faced with the issue.

EXPERIMENTAL AND/OR
UNPROVEN THERAPIES

All medical advances are the result of experiments. No procedure is known to be safe, or effective, the first time it is tried. Normally, experimental approaches are taken only when known approaches are unsuccessful with a given disorder.

When medications or other treatments for mental or other medical disorders are being investigated, researchers employ "double-blind" studies. This means that both the patients who are receiving the experimental treatment and the researchers who are evaluating the effects are not told who is getting the experimental drug and who is being given a "placebo," which looks the same but does not contain the medicine being tested. The objective of this procedure is to eliminate bias by either patients or researchers. (Sometimes patients feel better when they take a placebo because they think they are getting medicine to which they should be responding.)

Unfortunately, when patients—and their relatives—are desperate for help, they may place unwarranted confidence in experimental procedures or in downright quackery that succeeds, if at all, only on placebo effect. This attitude has persuaded many cancer patients and their families to go to foreign countries to obtain drugs that are il-legal in the United States because they have been proved to be medically ineffective. The same sort of hope can persuade mental patients and their relatives to pursue dietary and other purported biochemical panaceas that have not been proved effective against mental disorders.

The argument that biochemical abnormality causes many cases of mental disorder is no doubt true, but, in our current state of knowledge, we cannot say that the major psychotic disorders are correctable by diet alone. For example, attempts have been made to treat schizophrenia with large doses of niacin and other vitamins and minerals. Objective scientific tests have not proved this "megavitamin" treatment effective. Further, large doses of some vitamins and minerals can produce side effects.

Special diets and hormones have also been investigated, but currently there is no convincing scientific evidence that such treat-ment is curative. So-called "orthomolecular" psychiatrists have used vitamins and minerals in combination with antipsychotic medica-tions and have achieved good results, but it is difficult to determine how much of the improvement is due to something other than the antipsychotic medications.

Acupuncture is being studied as yet another approach to mental disorder. It is based on a very old approach to treatment of medical ill-ness, and it has shown some promising results, but the findings thus far are inconclusive.

There is much to be gained by exploring new approaches to treatment, and some of them will doubtless turn out to have validity and eventually replace current methods. What is important for you is to be objective in evaluating treatment for your relative.

The goal of the psychiatrist and the acute care psychiatric hospital is to help your relative get better as quickly as possible. Please keep this in mind, and avoid making judgments based on biases, wishful thinking, or conclusions derived from limited evidence (such as one person's experience). In your evaluation of what is best for your relative, try to put aside all predispositions and consider only the facts.

10

After The Patient
Leaves The Hospital

As we have seen in previous chapters, a number of people using a variety of approaches follow the treatment plan to reach various goals, which may be updated as the patient improves. Eventually, a time comes to think about discharging the patient. The prospects for continued improvement as an inpatient must be weighed against progress made to date, financial considerations, and other factors. Proper planning can help both the patient and the family prepare emotionally and practically for the patient's discharge.

Usually the patient will be on his or her own after discharge and will decide whether or not to pursue outpatient therapy. However, in some cases, patients will be regarded as requiring continued hospitalization (for example, because they are senile and unable to care for themselves) and will be transferred to a long-term facility. In other cases, further treatment on an involuntary basis may be arranged through a conservatorship, a guardianship, or a court order. For example, a patient who has been convicted of a crime may be given a choice between going to jail or undergoing continued psychiatric hospitalization at a long-term facility. Treatment may encourage rehabilitation through self-understanding and changes in behavior.

Especially with adolescents, courts often make an effort to turn the offender away from a lifetime of crime.

LONG-TERM FACILITIES AND OTHER STRUCTURED SETTINGS

If the patient is referred to another institution for further treatment, every attempt will be made to find the least restrictive setting that provides care appropriate to the patient's level of functioning. The range of available facilities depends to an extent on where you live, but different levels of structured settings are found virtually everywhere.

Long-term facilities for the disabled include those designed for psychiatric patients who have good physical health and others that also offer nursing care for medical problems. Some facilities focus on certain groups, such as geriatric patients or adolescents. Some facilities that treat the physically disabled offer skilled nursing care, while others provide only rudimentary help with feeding, bathing, dressing, and toileting. If you work with the staff of the referring acute care hospital in finding a placement, you may be able to visit several long-term facilities and take an active part in determining which one best serves your relative's needs, desires, and comfort.

Some long-term psychiatric hospitals offer fairly intensive treatment, either generally or for certain disorders, while others operate basically as convalescent homes. Motivation, severity of problems, willingness to seek treatment, and finances are important factors which determine where a patient should go. The more actively a patient can work on his or her problems and the greater the patient's strengths and capacity for progress, the more likely it is that he or she will be accepted at an institution that focuses on intensive work toward significant and lasting improvement. If a patient really does not want to be involved in psychotherapy, he or she will not be as welcome as someone with a greater chance of benefitting from the effort that the staff will be putting into the case. Some of the most highly esteemed long-term facilities do not accept involuntary patients under any circumstances.

Generally speaking, the greater your capacity to pay (whether through private funds or insurance coverage), the more options you will have. However, even if you do not have money or psychiatric insurance for long-term treatment, a public agency may arrange funding. Also, in most locales there is a state- or county-operated long-term facility that accepts patients without charge or at prices scaled to the person's ability to pay. Some of these institutions provide excellent treatment.

If a patient is both functional and highly motivated, he or she may not need hospitalization. Instead, he or she can become a resident in a halfway house, a residential treatment program, a group home, a rehabilitation center, or some other live-in setting where full-time supervision is available in an atmosphere that is more like that of a home than that of a hospital. However, in such facilities, residents must be willing to work actively on their problems and be able to get along with the other residents. Residents may be required to share such chores as cooking and cleaning. If so, this can reduce the number of employees necessary to care for them, and the commensurate savings may make it possible for the facility to charge considerably less than a full-care facility—and less than the resident is receiving in disability payments.

The more strongly an institution is oriented toward better functioning patients, the more is expected of a patient who is accepted to live there. At halfway houses, residents may require that prospective newcomers visit and perhaps eat dinner and spend the night so that everyone can assess whether the person is compatible with everyone else. When the decision to accept a newcomer is made, interviews by residents may be given considerably greater weight than recommendations from the referring hospital. Some halfway houses require ongoing formal outpatient therapy, and others also require that residents work actively toward a goal of independent living within a certain time.

Still other facilities are known by such names as "board and care" homes and specialize in providing meals, rooms, and supervision by a licensed operator for small groups of patients who cannot manage on their own immediately after discharge from an acute care psychiatric hospital. The staff looks after medication for residents who are unable to maintain a proper schedule on their own. Like halfway houses, many of these facilities require that residents be in outpatient psychotherapy and/or in one program or another that is designed to improve social skills and other abilities needed for everyday living.

Programs of the latter sort are available to, and usually are a good idea for, recently-discharged patients who want to live on their own in an apartment or hotel. The programs provide opportunities for socialization and recreation, relieving isolation and encouraging self-improvement. Once again, these programs are not designed for permanent placement.

OUTPATIENT THERAPY

Even if the patient is able to live comfortably on his or her own or with family and friends after being discharged from an acute care psychiatric hospital, continued therapy on an outpatient basis may be advisable.

The psychiatrist and other members of the hospital staff will, in planning the patient's discharge, take into account not only where the patient will live but also what kind of follow-up will ensure that the gains made during hospitalization will not be lost and that further progress will be made.

Initial outpatient treatment may include part-time hospitalization or day treatment that is similar to the hospital program. The program may be offered at the acute care hospital itself or at a separate facility. Treatment is geared toward socialization skills and coping with everyday problems in living. Other programs offer group activities and centers for learning living skills, including such basic activities as managing personal hygiene and meals. Many of these programs are relatively inexpensive or even free, because they are staffed not by employees but by dedicated and caring volunteers.

Much of the improvement that most patients experience in an acute care hospital may be due to medication, and if a patient stops taking it, or is unable to maintain the proper schedule, much of the progress that has been made might be reversed. Medication may be prescribed for a prolonged period, or the dosage may decline gradually until no medication is necessary. In either case, a psychiatrist must evaluate the patient's progress and perhaps make changes in the dosage or the medication itself as time passes. Some patients dislike taking medication and will stop as soon as they start feeling well. You can help your relative by being sure that he or she continues to take the prescribed medication. It is preferable for people to handle their problems without medication when possible, but often this is not possible until a patient has been taking medication for some time.

In earlier chapters I discussed patients' resistance to getting help. Fortunately, it often is much easier to convince a relative to continue therapy after leaving an acute care psychiatric hospital than it is to persuade him or her to enter the hospital. If outpatient treatment has been recommended, it is a good idea to get the patient into a program as soon as possible after discharge, not only to prevent a relapse but also to maintain the momentum of the patient's orientation to therapy that was built during hospitalization.

You may want to take part in some of the decisions about outpatient therapy—for example, selecting the psychotherapist or arranging the schedule. However, if the hospital's psychiatrist or other members of the treatment team believe that it would be better to give the patient the responsibility for making his or her own choices (and thereby feel more commitment to them), you should stand aside and not interfere.

Outpatient therapy may take place in the office of a psychotherapist who is in private practice or at a public clinic or agency. The choice of psychotherapist and setting will depend to a large extent on the variables of what is available where you live, the affordability of various programs, and what type of therapist the patient can work with most comfortably. Another consideration is how intense the treatment will be. For example, one patient will need nothing more than simple counseling about everyday problems, while another will need considerably more work in a number of areas.

In some programs, the psychotherapist's approach is mainly supportive. That is, the psychotherapist concentrates on being helpful to the patient but does not probe deeply, if at all, into the causes of the patient's problems. This may be because the patient does not need help of this kind or, in some cases, because there is not much opportunity for improvement, no matter what is done.

Other programs involve deep probing—referred to as "depth" psychotherapy. The psychotherapist delves into the patient's history and beliefs and motives, and tries to help the patient discover not only why certain patterns of behavior have developed but also how to develop more useful patterns. Unfortunately, depth therapy is possible only if the patient has the ability to tolerate frustration, to look at himself or herself critically and analytically, and to manage everyday functioning reasonably well.

Intensive therapy can be very expensive and can take a long time. Classical psychoanalysis, for example, usually requires daily or almost-daily visits for a number of years. Unlike hospital treatment, which tries to get a person functioning again as quickly as possible, psychoanalysis attempts to take apart mental life piece by piece in order to examine the components before reassembling them. However, while psychoanalysis and other intensive therapies are costly, they can be well worth all that they cost and more. We are, after all, talking about a person's life and the capacity to enjoy it.

Unlike inpatient treatment, which usually is fairly uniform in approach from one hospital to another, outpatient therapy offers a great variety of schools, goals, and techniques. The range of options may be bewildering to many people who have not had some training in psychology or allied subjects. Fortunately, however, you can get a referral from the psychiatrist who worked with your relative at the acute care hospital. Continuity of a given treatment approach is desirable, and the psychiatrist will know outpatient psychotherapists who share his or her therapeutic orientation. The psychiatrist also is well-equipped to take into account the patient's wishes, goals, and motivations.

The psychiatrist might recommend specialized therapy. For example, some clinics specialize in treatment of children and adolescents, while others specialize in treating the aged. In some localities, mental retardation programs operate independently of other elements of the mental health system. There are unique treatment approaches for children with learning disabilities, and special schooling may be needed. Counseling for delinquent children and their families may in some localities be offered by law enforcement agencies. Parents who have problems dealing with their children may be helped in group sessions with other parents, just as alcoholics and drug addicts may benefit from peer-group sessions.

There are yet other places to turn for support and help during your relative's early days after discharge. People at community mental health associations can be helpful in assisting you with your relative's problems. Also, special "case managers" at public agencies such as the local welfare office may be willing to help.

Friends and relatives are often crucially important in ensuring the success of follow-up therapy of a formerly hospitalized psychiatric patient. Let your relative's psychiatrist and other members of the treatment team know of your interest in the case and your eagerness to help, and they will offer advice on what specific things you should do.

For example, they may ask you to watch for certain symptoms that will indicate that something is going wrong. Or they may ask you to make sure that the patient does not stop taking medication. You may have to take over some of what used to be the patient's duties; for example, a husband may have to help with the shopping, cooking, and cleaning, which he had not done before his wife was hospitalized, or a wife may have to help with a husband's job.

Follow-up therapy may include family members other than the recently-discharged patient. Family therapy can improve communication between the patient and other members of the family, and it can help other members understand the patient's problem and offer support. Conjoint marital therapy may be appropriate if the spouses have been having marital problems or if the recently-discharged patient is regarded as potentially dangerous.

Once again, feel free to ask the hospital psychiatrist or other members of the treatment team for referrals and advice. You will not be "bothering" them. Having worked hard to help your relative get well, they are keenly interested in helping to ensure that he or she will stay well.

Afterword

If you have any questions as treatment goes along—or after your relative has been discharged—do not hesitate to ask them.

As your relative's treatment progresses, you may sometimes feel put off by things that he or she says. You may even get the impression that your relative resents your interest. However, even if he or she is severely disturbed and extremely abusive when you visit, the patient probably appreciates your visits more than you realize.

Do not worry about not knowing what to say or how to act. Trust your instincts. If you feel love, you will communicate love. And when your heart is in the right place, things usually have a way of working out.

If you work cooperatively with the members of the treatment team, it will make a tremendous difference in helping your relative get well again. Indeed, it may be the difference between your relative's going home again or being transferred to a long-term facility.

Be assured—I cannot say this too emphatically—that everyone on the treatment team appreciates a good relationship with relatives, because this makes everyone's job easier and more pleasant, and it also improves the prospects of successful treatment.

Once you have taken an interest in mental health as a result of helping your relative, you may be attracted to helping other patients and their families. Some hospitals have auxiliary groups of families of patients. Members of these groups offer each other support and understanding and work together for better treatment of the emotionally disturbed. For example, these groups can organize activities to get better funding for treatment, improve public understanding of the problems of mental patients, and reduce the stigma of mental illness.

The matter of funding is especially important, for the cost of hospitalization is more than most people can afford, and outpatient therapy—both before and after hospitalization—can be expensive, too. Yet, many insurance plans try to save money by cutting down on psychiatric benefits. Ironically, health costs often end up being higher as a result.

There are several reasons for this.

First of all, much expense can be avoided if proper treatment for emotional difficulties starts early, before problems become severe and extensive treatment—or even hospitalization—is needed. People are more likely to seek treatment promptly if their insurance covers it.

Second, many medical problems are really psychiatric problems in disguise, and much expensive medical treatment results from emotional problems that go unrecognized or unacknowledged. For example, such diseases as cirrhosis of the liver, gastrointestinal bleeding, and certain heart disorders are related to alcoholism, and their treatment uses up a huge portion of today's health-care dollar.

Moreover, time lost from work, lowered productivity, and disability caused by emotional or emotionally-related illnesses are very costly to individuals, to corporations, and to society as a whole.

The problem is not only a matter of dollars and cents. Think of the unhappiness and heartache that emotionally disturbed people cause by maiming and killing others by driving under the influence of alcohol or drugs. Think also of the loss of life, health, and property that results from crimes committed by drug addicts to support their habits.

If you believe that good insurance coverage for mental disorders is important, make your wishes known when it comes time to determine workers' benefits at your job or for an individual health plan. When shopping for personal or family health insurance, investigate fully the psychiatric benefits offered by different contracts—and read the small print, as in clauses that limit psychiatric hospitalization to a small number of days or that do not pay for outpatient therapy.

Of course, all insurance coverage has limits, and many people never own private insurance. When coverage is exhausted, public programs must take over. As virtually everyone knows, it has become harder and harder to get funding for public services, and many worthwhile causes compete for the limited funds available. So you must do as other groups do—make your wants and needs known.

You are a constituent of your elected officials. Together with other people facing similar problems, through mental health groups and similar organizations, you can work for better mental health funding. If you do not speak up, the needs of the mentally ill will continue to get short shrift—as historically they have.

So become politically aware. Find out what groups are in your area, join forces, and tell your legislators that you want adequate funding out of tax money for high-quality, humane treatment of these citizens who usually are not able to lobby effectively for themselves.

No one can predict who might need hospital treatment someday. It should be available when necessary. More money means the possibility of better treatment. You are concerned about your relative, and you want the best possible care. Making sure that it continues to be available is one of the most important things you can do to help.

Suggestions For Further Reading

If you would like to know more about your relative's treatment or about psychiatric diagnoses and approaches in general, there are a great many books that can broaden your understanding.

To get a real sense of what mental illness is like, read a book by someone who has gone through the experience, such as Hannah Green's *I Never Promised You a Rose Garden*.

If you want a glimpse of what psychotherapy is like from the therapist's standpoint, try *The Fifty Minute Hour*, by Robert Lindner, Ph.D.

For more information on where to turn for psychiatric help, especially as an outpatient, read *The Consumer's Handbook of Mental Health*, by Brian L. Mishara, Ph.D. and Robert D. Patterson, M.D., or *You Are Not Alone*, by Clara Claiborne Park, with Leon N. Shapiro, M.D.

To become familiar with a specific diagnosis, consult such books as *Up From Depression*, by Leonard Cammer, M.D.

For more detailed discussion of psychiatric conditions, consult such works as the *Comprehensive Textbook of Psychiatry*, edited by Harold I. Kaplan, M.D.; Alfred M. Freedman, M.D.; and Benjamin J. Sadock, M.D. This text, aimed at psychiatrists and students of psychiatry, is nonetheless very clearly written. Even though you may not have a background in medicine, you probably will find that you can understand much of its contents. (If you cannot find it at a public library, you should be able to find it at a university library.)

For more information about the brain and neurology, consult the excellent illustrations and text in the *Nervous System*, by Frank Netter, M.D.

For background on the development of psychiatric treatment and also for the original thinking of the pioneers of psychiatry, consult such primary sources as the *Collected Works of Sigmund Freud* or Otto Fenichel's *Psychoanalytic Theory of the Neurosis*. Some of these works may prove inaccessible but others are fairly easy to understand, such as Georg Groddeck's *Book of the It*.

These are a few of what I think are the best books on each subject. If you have a special interest in any of these subjects and would like to read about it in greater detail, bibliographies within the books that I have recommended will supply you with quite a few additional references.

To find a great many other psychiatry-related books that may interest you, simply browse libraries and bookstores or solicit recommendations from friends and from mental health professionals.

Index